All of Us
Apes

AND OTHER
SCIENTIFIC WISDOM FROM

Ockham's Razor

All Us Apes

AND OTHER SCIENTIFIC WISDOM FROM

Ockham's Razor

INTRODUCTION BY

ROBYN WILLIAMS

an
ABC
BOOK

Published by ABC Books for the
AUSTRALIAN BROADCASTING CORPORATION
GPO Box 9994 Sydney NSW 2001

National Library of Australia
Cataloguing-in-Publication entry
All us apes and other scientific wisdom from Ockham's razor.

ISBN 0 7333 0533 4.

1. Science - Popular works. 2. Science - Radio scripts.
I. Williams, Robyn. II. Australian Broadcasting Corporation.
III. Title: Ockham's razor (Radio program).

500

Cover designed by Toni Hope-Caten
Set in 9/13½ pt Garamond Light by
Midland Typesetters, Maryborough, Victoria
Colour separations by First Media, Adelaide
Printed and bound in Australia by
Australian Print Group, Maryborough, Victoria

5 4 3 2 1

CONTENTS

INTRODUCTION

———————

Every now and then it is necessary for producers such as me to justify to the boss the things that we do. In this case it was to Peter Manning, now no longer with the ABC but once, famously, the general manager of Radio National.

He wanted to know about this odd thing: a 'scripted talk', which surely went down at the fall of Singapore, with all the other relics of another age—Noel Coward, Russell Braddon, the Gin Sling. Why was I so keen that it continue and why did it do so well in the RN ratings lists?

I said something about 'the voice of Australians distilled after reflection' and the 'variety of considered opinion', but then just left a few tapes for him to listen to. Nothing remarkable, the ones from the previous month.

His reaction, a few days later has always stayed with me. He said simply, 'It makes us all sound so bloody intelligent!' Then he returned the tapes. On we went.

Ockham's Razor is a science program—broadly speaking—and it is named after the gentle friar who, six hundred years ago, advised that the simplest explanations for natural phenomena are probably the best. It has been on for twelve years and almost runs itself. This does not mean it is easy work for Brigitte Seega and me, but we certainly do not have to seek desperately for people wanting to have their say. This is what the Jeremiahs warned would be our biggest problem in the beginning.

Some do just one talk and leave it at that. Others do more; Tony Barnett, professor emeritus at the Australian National University, for example, who did his first broadcast on the BBC when I was minus two, has done twenty-three. Barry Jones was invited to have a go at Ockham's Razor when his book *Sleepers, Wake!* was first published. He did two. On the release of the fourth edition almost fifteen years later he returned for another go.

We have, sadly, lost old friends. One was Dr Bill Williams, the 'barefoot botanist' from Townsville in Northern Queensland, who expounds movingly on how his devoted dog helped save his life when once he lay in coma. It is a wry tribute to Bill's sense of humour to record that he died in October, 1995, from a blow to the head, after tripping over his dog's lead in a pub.

The talks come from all over Australia and from young or old. That is the point, may I say, of public service broadcasting. We seek out good ideas, not high station, so the presenters may be eminent or in the early spring of their careers. And I do believe that the audience response comes from a relishing of that unexpected element combined with an appreciation of considered argument.

This is quite different from that other source of *vox populi*: the dreaded 'phone-in'. The latter is reactive and improvised, often irritatingly so. Scripted talks enable us, on the other hand, to show how very thoughtful we are, as a nation. And Peter Manning was right: 'so bloody intelligent'.

Robyn Williams

All Us
Apes
AND OTHER
SCIENTIFIC WISDOM FROM

Ockham's Razor

PHILOSOPHY AND THE
PARANORMAL

WILLIAM GREY

WILLIAM GREY is a Senior Lecturer in Philosophy at the University of Queensland and a member of Australian Skeptics. He has been a sceptic in all his previous incarnations.

Some of you may not know how philosophy is conducted at a university, so I will begin with a short account of the nature and aims of philosophical inquiry. 'Philosophy' is a word we have taken from the Greek, which means 'love of wisdom'. But what is wisdom? A fellow philosopher and friend of mine has nicely explained 'wisdom' as follows:

> If we were lost in a maze, it would be a great advantage to us to be able to climb on to a platform and gain a new point of view— an overview—from which we could discover which way we are going and the best way to get there. Typically a wise person is one who can provide us with such an overview. What wise people do . . . is . . . help us to see our problem from a fresh point of view. By doing so they put the problem in perspective; they allow us to see where alternative courses of action would lead, and in doing

so, they put us in a better position to see which course of action is preferable. In general, philosophers seek wisdom because it provides them with a point of view from which they can see more clearly what the options for living are. (David Ward, 'Being Human and Being Rational')

This little story nicely illustrates how philosophy can increase our understanding by widening our horizons. The sort of wisdom philosophers seek is explained here as *practical* wisdom; that is, it attempts to provide an answer to the problem (raised long ago by Socrates): 'How should one live?' But we also seek wisdom when we try to deepen our understanding of what the world is like. Wisdom is bound up with an increase or *enrichment* of our understanding of ourselves or the world, and how we might best live in that world. How can we set about the task of becoming wise?

If we want a clear and accurate understanding of the world we need to eliminate inconsistent and false beliefs. Supposing that the Earth is flat, or that a pure water diet will cure pneumonia, may have serious practical consequences. Evidence may mislead us seriously, or even fatally; it is usually important to be right.

Seeking to match our belief to the available evidence is one way of introducing *epistemology*, which is a branch of philosophy which deals with the nature of knowledge and belief, and the problem of matching belief to evidence. Another fundamental branch of philosophy which I need to mention is *metaphysics*, which is concerned to provide an account of the basic structure of reality. The Cambridge philosopher Charles Dunbar Broad pointed out that we habitually and unconsciously assume at least five metaphysical assumptions in interpreting our experience of the world. These are, firstly, that future events cannot affect the present before they happen (what is going to happen tomorrow can't make anything happen today); second, that a person's mind cannot effect a change in the material world without the intervention of some physical energy or force; third, that a person cannot know the content of another person's mind except by the use of inferences based on experience and drawn from observations of their speech or behaviour; fourth, that we cannot directly know what happens at distant points in space without some sensory perception or energy of it transmitted to us; and fifth, that discarnate beings do not exist as persons separable from physical bodies.

Science provides strong support for each of these assumptions, and so far no one has provided any reliable, replicable evidence against any one of them. But each of these assumptions is called into question by 'paranormal' claims. The paranormal therefore provides an interesting challenge to some central metaphysical assumptions about what the world is like, and it also raises a basic problem about our knowledge of the world, because it claims that we have good reason to think that, in some important respects, scientific knowledge is either incomplete or fundamentally mistaken.

Our problem is that we are told by some people (psychics and clairvoyants, for example) that we have good reason to believe that what science tells us about the world is wrong. And the scientists tell us that the pronouncements of the friends of the paranormal are a tissue of fantasy, error, self-deception, wishful thinking and fraud.

We might hope that philosophy can say something useful in this sort of predicament, when we are confronted with conflicting testimony. The scientists might be wrong, or the psychics might be wrong—indeed, they *both* might be wrong (though one side might be *more* wrong than the other). But they can't both be *right*. Can we get an overview? A perspective which will help to throw some light on these conflicting claims?

The first point to note is that there is a difference between doubt and disbelief. If someone presents what they believe to be compelling evidence that something will happen, say that it will snow in Brisbane next Christmas, or that plants grow better in anti-magnetic fields, but

I don't believe the evidence is sufficient, I don't have to conclude that it won't snow in Brisbane, or that the plants won't grow. I can just say that the evidence isn't good enough, at this stage, to settle the matter definitely either way. Scepticism is a matter of *doubt* rather than *denial*.

In fact this is the characteristic stance of scepticism. A sceptic is someone who calls a knowledge claim into question. (Scepticism, please note, is *not* the same as cynicism.) Being sceptical (that is, withholding assent, or suspending belief in a particular claim) need *not* involve believing the opposite. Scepticism is *dogmatic* if assent is withheld on the basis of prior conviction without considering the evidence. Scepticism is *global* if it encompasses *all* claims to knowledge; *selective* if it is targeted to specific knowledge claims. Many of our beliefs, such as those about the content and composition of immediate surroundings, are relatively immune to sceptical doubts. You don't doubt the existence of chairs and tables in your vicinity, or the paper in front of you on which these words are written. Other beliefs (such as claims about tooth fairies and Santa Claus) we dismiss without hesitation. Between these extremes are disputed cases—such as God or economic rationalism; and also psychic and paranormal phenomena.

The *undogmatic* variety of scepticism, which I call *critical* scepticism, means keeping an open mind and not rejecting disputed claims *a priori*. It involves refusing to accept as true claims for which there is insufficient or ambiguous evidence, and recognising that withholding belief is preferable to accepting claims for which there are not sufficient grounds. Scepticism is all about matching belief to evidence. It adopts a methodological maxim that in seeking explanations we should prefer the ordinary to the extraordinary, and the simple to the complex. This maxim is sometimes identified with a principle attributed to the fourteenth century philosopher William of Ockham, and called 'Ockham's Razor'.

There are some intriguing parallels between the structure of scientific explanations and the structure of psychic explanations. However I don't have time to go into this interesting story. Instead I'm going to sketch the wisdom of an eighteenth century Scottish empirical philosopher and historian, David Hume, who thoughtfully addressed in his essay 'Of Miracles', some two and a half centuries ago, a problem which is in many ways analogous to the one which claims of the paranormal raise for us now.

What should we do when confronted with claims which are conspicuously at odds with the general run of experience? That's the problem which the paranormal presents for us, and it's the problem which *miracles* presented for Hume.

Paranormal phenomena are events which appear to be quite astonishing—frequently at odds with well-established laws of nature. And the violation of a law of nature is precisely Hume's definition of a miracle. That is, paranormal claims raise for us exactly the same epistemological problems which Hume addressed around 250 years ago.

After looking at the credentials for miraculous claims, Hume came to the conclusion that the balance of probabilities counted against them. Hume was aware of the impossibility of proving a negative: there is no way that he could prove that miracles simply never happen. But he developed an ingenious argument to show something a little different, which he believed would be of considerable consequence: that is, that *it is never rational to believe that miracles have occurred.* Hume was concerned, then, with an *epistemological* question of what it is and is not rational to believe, rather than a metaphysical argument about what sorts of events can happen in our sort of world.

Hume's argument has two stages. First he argued that the evidence against miracles is usually very strong. In arguing for this, Hume proposes a principle which has been called Hume's Razor. As Hume put it in 'Of Miracles':

No testimony is sufficient to establish a miracle unless that testimony be of such a kind that its falsehood would be more miraculous than the fact which it endeavours to establish.

Hume here is arguing that if we are asked to believe something which appears to be extremely improbable, we should in turn ask, *which* is more probable: that the improbable event happened, or that the testimony supporting this improbable event is mistaken. Only when the evidence is so solid as to be beyond dispute should we accept it as warranting belief in the contested event. This is a basic ground rule which is repeatedly illustrated in scientific practice; it continues, for example in the current dispute about 'cold fusion' initiated by Pons and Fleischman. Scientific inquiry is the systematic deployment of critical scepticism.

Though the evidential standards we demand to substantiate extraordinary claims are high, they are *not*—and should not be—impossibly high. If the evidence was good enough, we could be persuaded. (A sceptic who refuses in advance to consider evidence is a *dogmatic* sceptic.)

The second step of Hume's argument is his claim that, at least in the case of miracles, the evidence just isn't good enough. For even though the evidence in favour of miracles *might* outweigh the evidence against them, in practice *this never happens*.

There are four factors which Hume believed (severally and together) undermine the credibility of any miraculous claim. Firstly, witness credibility: witnesses for miracles have frequently turned out to be unreliable and mistaken. And the same it must be said has turned out to be true for witnesses for the paranormal in our time. Second, human credulity—which Hume called 'the love of wonder'. People have a great appetite for extraordinary tales, as a short research trip to your local newsagent will readily confirm. Third, there is the fact that many superstitions have been derived from relatively unsophisticated cultures. As Hume put it in his eighteenth century ethnocentric manner, belief in the miraculous is usually derived from our 'barbarous and ignorant ancestors'. And finally, different cultural traditions generate insoluble conflicts of testimony: for any miraculous claim, there is an equally good tradition which *denies* that miraculous claim. Thus Christianity denies Islamic miracles, and vice versa.

I repeat that Hume did *not* say that he had shown that miracles never occur. He knew that he had done no such thing. Rather, he claimed that it would never be rational to suppose that miracles *do* occur. He was proposing an empirical argument (that is, an argument based on factual claims) against the credibility of miracles.

Some, though not all of Hume's points apply to claims about the paranormal. We should, in the spirit of Hume, demand high evidential standards before accepting paranormal claims. We should also be aware of the way that the love of wonder can now, as it did in Hume's time, pervert the search for truth. (Incidentally, I don't think Hume would have been astonished at the continuing level of credulity at the close of the twentieth century.)

Like Hume we should be critically (though not dogmatically) sceptical when we are confronted with claims that something truly astonishing has occurred. Astonishing claims include a whole raft of claims about so-called New Age phenomena which may embrace such things as telepathy, precognition, clairvoyancy, water divining, levitation, astral travelling, channelling, UFO abductions, faith healing, or healing by alternative medicine. When confronted with such claims we should follow Hume's wise example and ask whether it is more probable that the alleged effect or event *really* occurred or occurs, or whether its proponents were somehow deceived, or mistaken. Or it may be that the event which appeared quite extraordinary, turns out to be not as extraordinary as it appeared at first sight, and that the event which appeared to be anomalous, has a perfectly natural explanation—as is the case, for example, with firewalking.

I have presented Hume's position very schematically. Of course it is necessary to address individual claims on a case-by-case basis. But we should, in the spirit of Hume, refuse to accept paranormal claims unless powerful and compelling evidence is presented to substantiate them.

VENICE AND THAT
SINKING FEELING

GEORGE SEDDON

GEORGE SEDDON is an Honorary Senior Research Fellow in the Centre for Studies in Australian Literature at the University of Western Australia.

One of the world's most remarkable achievements in environmental management and urban design is that of Venice and the Venetian Republic. It is a great story of adaptation by men to the exigencies of a special and in many ways very difficult environment, and also of the adaptation of the environment itself to man's own special needs, which in this case included an insatiable thirst for quality in the city buildings—all of them, not just those of the wealthy.

All the world recognises the beauty of Venice, but the long, sustained effort to adapt and manage the lagoon and its hinterland is not at all well known. It was one of the finest examples of landscape planning in the broad sense for well over a thousand years. Only in the last 140 years or so have all the lessons been forgotten.

One primary objective, pursued from the thirteenth century onwards, was to stabilise the lagoon. Lagoons are essentially ephemeral features; their usual fate is to be filled in by river-borne sediment. Venice itself is built on the remnants of the delta of the Brenta River, flooded by rising sea-levels at the end of the Ice Age. Over the centuries, the Venetians systematically diverted the rivers (by pick and shovel) to the north and south of the lagoon; the major ones diverted to the south were the Brenta, which delivers more water than the Murray, and the much smaller Bachiglione, which runs through Palladio's city of Vicenza (my favourite city in Italy); to the north, the Sile, Treviso's delightful little river, and the Piave, another major river, rising in the East Tyrol, and the site of bloody battles during the First World War. The ways in which these great engineering feats were executed were ingenious: for example, the Sile was diverted by canal into what had been the bed of the Piave, and then into the sea near Jesolo, while the Piave itself was diverted into the bed of the next river to the north, the Livenza.

The tides could not wholly be regulated—disastrous high tides, *le acque alte*, have occurred sporadically throughout Venetian history—but they were controlled in some measure by strengthening the sea walls of the *lidi*, the sand bars that fringe the lagoon on its seaward side. The many entrances between these lidi were in time limited to three; these are the Chioggia, Malamocco and Lido entrances. The sea walls were the last of the great works of the Magistrates of the Waters. They were begun in 1744, took thirty-eight years to complete, and cost some forty million Venetian gold ducats—hardly surprising, since they were built of great blocks of white marble brought from Istria across the Adriatic, the customary Venetian source of marble. These walls are around 5 metres thick at the base, and some 7 metres high, replacing wooden palisades that needed constant repair.

Venetian hydraulic engineering was not perfect, and there were costs, but it worked adequately for most of the history of the Republic. One cost was their elimination of one of the distributaries of the mighty Po, the Po di Tramontana, which emptied into the lagoon north of Chioggia at the southern end of the lagoon. It delivered vast quantities of silt, and was rapidly turning its environs into a *laguna morta*, flooded only at high tides, stinking mud through the rest of the cycle. In five years, thousands of labourers cut the Sacca di Goro, a channel from the Po Grande, the main river distributary, into a bay of the Adriatic east of Pomposa, and water no longer drained through the Po di Tramontana into the lagoon. The results for the lower Po valley and the Delta were disastrous; silting accelerated, the Delta increased three times in area in two hundred years, and the severity of flooding increased. But none of that worried the Venetians. They had protected their own lagoon.

Perhaps they protected it too well. One school of hydrologists today argue that at least some incoming sediment was desirable to compensate for the lowering of the lagoon floor consequent on compaction under the weight of centuries of deposition. There certainly is a problem today, but its origins are complex, and the system of management by diversion worked well for nearly one thousand years. It was essential to Venice, and she knew it. She had close at hand the example of Ravenna, a great Roman and Byzantine seaport, now high and dry. The Venetians, moreover, were sailors and they knew the great cities along the Aegean coast, such as Ephesus and Miletus, long beached like stranded whales.

The lagoon was her chief defence, and she was never invaded until Napoleon ended the Republic. It was also her only transport system, both externally and internally. Finally, it was her major source of protein: seafood sustained the Venetians. The level of the tides has always been critical to her functioning, as Ruskin shows so well in *The Stones of Venice*; a few inches lower at low tide, and Venice begins to stink, many canals are no longer navigable, and the lower landing steps become intolerably slimy; a few inches higher at high tide and water would come in the doorways, the level becomes too high to get under many of the bridges, and the buildings begin to erode. That is part of what is happening now. Venice may be sinking. It is certainly eroding.

It is besieged by a range of problems. First, there are *le acque alte*, the exceptionally high tides. These are sporadic natural events, a recurrent feature of Venetian history, always destructive and costly. They generally happen when the spring tides or naturally high tides coincide with strong and persistent winds from the southeast—the sirocco—which push and funnel the sea water up the Adriatic between Italy and Croatia. The horrific floods of 1966 were of this kind, exaggerated further by exceptionally heavy rain throughout much of northern Italy. The water reached 2 metres higher than normal high tide level, the Piazza San Marco was under water, and waves were breaking against the Ducal Palace. The damage was estimated at forty billion lire.

This was nevertheless an extreme event—recurrent, but infrequent. Various remedies have been proposed, and a good deal of money spent on inflatable barrages, designed to block the three entries of the lagoon when exceptionally high tides threaten. But there are other, less dramatic, but more insidious, problems. One is chemical corrosion, both from sulphur dioxide and other pollutants in the air, which attack the very stones of Venice, and from similar industrial and domestic pollutants in the water and the mud. Venice is built on piles driven into the mud. Great logs cut from chestnut trees have lasted well in the anaerobic environment of the mud, but now it is heavily laced with chemicals which may be beginning to attack the piles.

There was subsidence attributed to the withdrawal of water from some 20 000 deep artesian wells, used to supply the city and industry on the mainland. Many of these wells are now capped and water is supplied by aqueduct. There may also be slow subsidence of the lagoon floor caused by long-term compaction of the great layered wedge of sediment that underlies it. The lagoon floor is certainly being lowered, but whether this has one or several concurrent causes is not clear. It is undoubtedly subject to erosion, and this seems to me to be the key problem.

Why should the lagoon floor be eroding? In brief, because no sediment is coming in to replace the sediment now lost daily by tidal scour. The rivers remain diverted. Sand from longshore drift, which once balanced tidal scour, no longer enters the lagoon because of the long moles protecting the three entrances to the lagoon. And tidal velocity is much greater, because the ship channels have been deepened (Malamocco to 13 metres, the Lido-Guidecca channel to 11 metres). Moreover, one-quarter of the tidal marshes, which used to dissipate tidal energy, have been filled—for industrial land at Porto Marghera, for the new airport Marco Polo, and so on. Thus more water rushes in and out during the period of the tide, into a significantly reduced lagoon, from which the natural baffles of reed and marsh have been almost eliminated.

Venice conserved and managed its other natural resources as well as it managed the lagoon, and for the same reason—it knew it needed to. The myth of an inexhaustibly bountiful Nature was never a part of the Venetian world view. For instance, she needed a constant supply of good timber for ship-building at the Arsenale, chestnut for the galleys, beech for the oars. Her only reliable sources were the forests above the Canale di Brenta and the Altipiano di Asiago and Monte Grappa, and these forests were conserved with great care throughout the Republic. The forests of Dalmatia also supplied timber, but less reliably. Timber was always in short supply, but that was seen as a reason for conserving it rather than over-producing from a wasting resource. The chestnut forests of the Brenta lasted until after the Second World War. They were then all felled within twenty years and are not now regenerating. Fishing was regulated. Stone came from the quarries at Istria and the Euganean Hills, transported through a canal system. Stone is not a renewable resource, but the quarries were regulated. The country estates with their Palladian villas—such as Villa Barbaro a Maser, the Pisani Villa at Stra, La Malcontenta, both on the Brenta, Villa Contarini, and so on—were well managed, and the estate

13

workers were generally well cared for by the standards of the day.

The city itself and urban life was also well regulated, by the most stable government Europe has ever known, on which the American constitution was substantially modelled. Urban scale was preserved by regulations on building height. Civic and social life were accommodated in the public open spaces—*campi*—which came in all sizes from the Piazza San Marco to the Piazzetta dei Leoni, Campo Luca, Campo Santo Stefano of middling size, and small ones like the Campo S. Lio. There were also internal courtyards. These spaces allowed light into the buildings and air circulation, and they collected water in the central well. The markets were well run, and civic administration was at a high level. Venice instituted the census, and maintained it for hundreds of years. Taxes were fair. It was a tolerant city; Venice never burned a heretic. Its urban services were, and still are in many ways, a marvel of adaptive talent. The taxis, the ambulance, the fire brigade, the police, all go by water.

It was, and still is, mostly a 'hard' landscape, made of stone and water, although there is a surprising number of private gardens full of greenery. Street trees are rare although the zattere at Dorsoduro are lined with Russian olive and standard oleander, almost trees, and years old. There is no *cosmetic* landscaping, and this is perhaps the most important design lesson Venice has to teach. Get the functional relations right, the scale, the spaces, the proportions. They are what create good urban landscape.

Today, it has nearly all gone wrong. The lagoon is heavily polluted and eutrophic, the fishing is in decline, the city is eroding and decaying, the chestnut forests have been felled, the Veneto is subject to a vast monoculture of maize, the sick fields are suffering from an overdose of superphosphate, so the canals are clogged with green algae, which decay and stink, the very underpinning of the city is under attack, and that splendidly resilient civic pride has gone; all is now geared to the tourists, who swarm like locusts. Mountains of their garbage in its hundreds of thousands of plastic bags is carried out to sea and dumped daily, into that self-same Adriatic to which Venice once renewed her marriage vows yearly with a gold ring, the marriage bed now a garbage dump.

There is adequate knowledge to understand most of these problems and to offer solutions. For example, the eutrophication is due to excessive use of superphosphate on the plains of Lombardy. We have encountered similar problems in some of our estuaries, and tackled them, and are on the way to solving them—in the Peel-Harvey Inlet, for instance. I have explained to the Venetians that we are much better at solving the problems of incompetent agriculture in Australia because we have been practising it longer. But the Venetians hardly know where to begin, because there is now no policital-administrative system that corresponds to the Plains of Lombardy; an informal association began to emerge only last year, to tackle common problems. But even if it were strong, there is no equivalent in Italy to the field officers of our Departments of Agriculture, who can go the rounds and talk to each farmer. In any case, the current form of agribusiness is itself the outcome of a political system, the EEC, which is heavily protectionist.

The solution to the erosion is to close Porto Marghera or drastically to reduce ship size, to fill in the deep channels, and probably also to re-excavate some of the filled land and to shorten the moles to allow some sediment to be carried in once again by longshore drift. One could even dump sand from barges, but it is always better to harness natural processes where that is feasible. Most Italian ports are suffering from decline. As Europe has turned inwards, transport has moved to heavy lorries—not a wise choice. As the environmental costs become more obvious, there will surely be a new investment in rail-freighting; the passenger trains have already had their renaissance. The ports too may revive one day, but there is no sound future for Porto Marghera.

As for mass tourism—the answer is simple. Restrict entry, as we now do to many national parks, after determining their carrying capacity. Yosemite is one; even Wilsons Promontory has a strict ration of camp sites other than that of Tidal River, and would-be backpackers need to book long in advance to get one of the seven sites at Roaring Meg, for instance.

Can we learn anything from Venice, or is it so special as to be irrelevant to our circumstances? If we acknowledge that Venice is in itself a lesson in urban landscape, we can still ask 'What is the lesson?' We are in part asking about pathways and forces, in part about shared community values, in part about the way in which a shared design framework evolved, to which many could contribute without that restless striving for originality and the immediately distinctive that characterises so much design today. The concentration on the central functional relations is probably the key. Design marginalises itself if it is concerned primarily with palliatives, as it so often is. Words like 'screen' or 'conceal' or 'soften' all indicate this approach. For example, we would not need to 'soften' buildings with trees if we got the buildings and the spaces right. Cities ought not to strive to be gardens, or rather, they should strive first to be cities. Certainly the Garden City is not the only model for urban landscape design.

EDUCATING RITA

JONATHAN STONE

JONATHAN STONE is Challis Professor of Anatomy at the University of Sydney.

I don't know how or why a scene from an old movie sticks hidden in one's memory, to reappear unbidden years later in a strange context, but it happened to me last week. The movie was *Educating Rita*, and it must be five years ago that I saw it. The heroine was a feisty, funny girl from Liverpool who—over her husband's protests—went off to get educated at a university, where she encountered a disillusioned and besozzled Michael Caine. Coming home from university one weekend, she was greeted most warmly by her husband and—and in the scene I recalled—she excused herself for a moment to reach into a secret compartment under the bedroom floor, where she kept her contraceptives. Her scrabbling was furtive and a bit slapstick; clearly her husband wasn't meant to know.

The scene was cheerful, a bit farcical, and a bit serious too, for it drew its tension from the heroine's determination not to fall pregnant, and her husband's view that Nature should be allowed to take its course. One strand of the film's story, in fact, concerned the effect of education on Rita; how, having seen broader horizons, she could no longer be content with the settled but narrow working-class community in which she had grown up and married. To have a child,

Rita realised, would close off her opportunity to finish her degree and to escape from the life she had come to reject.

I had been reading a book, an excellent book, but not one that was funny or farcical or Liverpudlian, nor about education, nor likely to be made into a movie. Its title was a handicap for a start—*The Future of Low Birthrate Populations*. Its author is a distinguished demographer, interested in human populations, their size, their past, their future, their rates of birth and death, their age breakdown and so on. It sounds a bit dry, but if we do not understand what is happening to our population we will fail the major challenge of our future, to find a way for our species to live within the resources available to us.

We all, I guess, have some impression of the world's population, if only because those counting boards outside museums around the world have made us all conscious of its seemingly inexorable growth. Every year the human population of the planet increases by 90 to 100 million, and we are crowded already, and polluted, and the rainforests are dwindling and we are destroying other species. So why would anyone spend energy now on a book about low-birthrate populations?

I don't mean to criticise our museums, but human populations are complex things, too complex to be represented by a single figure. Yes, the population of the world will increase by 100 million this year, and we have too many people already. But the following propositions are also true:

- The birthrate among humans—the number of children born per woman—has been falling worldwide for over fifty years, and in Europe for over a century.
- The birthrate is now lower than at any time in our history.
- The rate of population growth has been falling for about twenty-five years (it peaked at 2.1 per cent in 1965–70, and has now eased back to 1.7 per cent).
- Throughout western Europe, and in a number of eastern European

countries and, incidentally, in Australia, birthrates are well below replacement rates.

• In some countries of middle Europe—Scandinavian countries and western Germany—populations are already shrinking.

How can we reconcile all this with the inexorable climb of the museum's numbers? Well, birthrates are falling throughout the world, but their falls were everywhere preceded by massive falls in death rates. Because death rates fell first, more children are reaching adulthood to bear their own children and more adults are surviving into their eighties. The result is a massive growth in population. Second, the growth in population is far from uniform across the world; almost all population growth is occurring in Africa, Asia and South America. The population of Europe has stabilised, and seems set to fall, and it was of Europe that this author was writing. Now it took several generations for birthrates in Europe to fall from the high levels of 40/1000/year—the value seen in most undeveloped societies—to the level of 10–15/1000/year now found throughout western Europe, and it takes at least two generations of below-replacement birthrates before the population actually starts to fall. Europe, Asia and Africa are all on the same population course, but the process began in Europe half a century before it spread to Africa or Asia. Europe, in short is 'ahead of the world' in the important mission of not having babies. This process, in which first death rates and then birthrates fall from high levels to low, has been given a name by demographers—it is called the demographic transition. It holds out the hope—I suspect our only hope—that within a century the population of the world will stabilise, although at very high levels, and then start to fall. It is thus of enormous importance for our future.

What does all this have to do with Rita? Well, it has become clear that the falls in fertility which characterise the demographic transition—and which are the most marked ever known in our history—

are not organised by government, nor by social movements, nor by religions. They result from the private decisions of young couples to have fewer children than their parents. We do not know how often it is a joint decision, and how often it is the woman who—like Rita—decides for herself. But the effects of these millions of separate decisions are quietly dramatic—the closure of schools because of low enrolments, the adaptation of housing architecture to smaller families, the greater provision of goodies for the fewer children who are born, and eventually a shrinking population.

Why is it happening? That is most interesting. A woman's decision to have fewer children than her mother is not simply linked to contraceptive technology—though she will certainly use that technology. Historically, the trend began in the 1850s, long before there was a technology of contraception. Nor is Rita's decision much influenced by religion—birthrates in Catholic Italy are as low as anywhere else in Europe. Nor is she influenced by her government, for no Western government has a population policy; nor is she likely to have been influenced by private groups concerned with population, which have emerged only very recently. Nor is her decision simply related to her affluence, as some of our industrial leaders would have it; for birthrates fall sharply in economic depressions and in times of war, and bounce up when depressions and wars have ended.

What then does influence the decisions of couples to have fewer children? The parents among you might say—well it's obvious, Rita wants to be something as well as mother. I suspect you are right, but to a biologist, Rita's decision is revolutionary. When we study the reproductive decisions of most animals, it is clear that they have as many offspring as they can manage and, in many species, far more than can be expected to survive. A few mechanisms which limit procreation of animals have been identified—for example, poor nutrition of the mother will increase intervals between offspring, and so will extended suckling. But most animals behave as though their mission in life is to produce as many offspring as possible, and in our heredity and structure and function, we too are animals. Each woman has thousands of potential eggs in her ovaries, far more than the 400 she will release during her reproductive life, and that number is far more than she could possibly bring to term; and more again than are needed to replace her and her partner. It is striking to see women turn away from the evolutionary imperative, to maximise the survival of her genes, and instead make her decisions on behaviourist lines, to maximise her personal development.

It is just as well that women have taken these decisions; if birthrates had stayed at their historical average of 40/1000/year found at the beginning of the Industrial Revolution, while death rates fell as they have, Earth's population would already have reached 10 billion and our environmental crisis would be more urgent than it is; indeed, catastrophe would probably be upon us already. Thomas Malthus' grim vision that the human population of the planet would grow to the limits of its food supply—to starvation, in short—would be part of our times, not just a threat in our future. We already owe women a great debt.

We are left with a question. We've been around as a species for over 10 000 years; why have women changed the basis of their reproductive decisions only in recent decades? There are, it turns out, as many answers to that question as there are demographers. Some argue that when parents gain confidence in the survival of their children they choose to have fewer; or that compulsory schooling reduces the economic value of children by keeping them out of the work force; or that the sheer cost of raising a child in the middle class is too daunting. Others argue—and this is my preferred explanation—that the most consistent correlate of a woman's decision to limit her family is the level of her education. The more knowledge of the world she has, the more she will be able to control the number of children she has; and it would seem, the more she will want to limit her offspring, so that she can maximise her own potential as an individual.

That scene I remembered from *Educating Rita* may have been comical, but it touched a quiet revolution of our times, with two important implications for our future. One is that, however sensible it may seem to fight overpopulation by birth control programs, a far better return for investment will be achieved by the education of women, ensuring that girls throughout the world get at least four years' education, and preferably more. Educate her, the lesson seems to be, and she will reduce her fertility. The second implication is that women, who I suspect play more than an equal share in decisions over family size, are a key factor in the future of our species. If women worldwide maintain their current trend of slowly reducing the size of their families, world population will plateau out at 12 billion sometime in the second half of the next century. If they move more quickly (so that the rate of fall in fertility is doubled), population could level off at 10 billion; and that difference may be the difference between a controlled and a catastrophic end to human overpopulation, especially in Africa and Asia. If, on the other hand, women move more slowly than we expect and the fall in fertility slows by half, world population will move towards 20 billion, and catastrophe seems inevitable.

Much of our future lies then with the decisions of the women of today and tomorrow to limit their families. Women have already done much to limit the planet's population, and they deserve every support and encouragement in those decisions. What, incidentally, are the problems of low birthrate populations? Well, there will be problems, as the author—Lincoln Day of the Australian National University—points out. They will have a high proportion of old people needing care, a smaller proportion of the population in the work force, lots of highly cared-for single children, fewer brothers and sisters, fewer aunts and uncles. And there will be uncertainty about their future. It is most unlikely that any human community will restrict its birthrate until it shrinks to insignificance, but we can only guess at the level at which populations will stabilise. Nevertheless children of such self-limiting populations will have more space and opportunity, and more hope of a decent life than children in a population which grows until it starves.

We rely much on Rita.

MIND OF THE
MATHEMATICIAN

SUE WOOLFE

SUE WOOLFE is the author of the novel *Leaning Towards Infinity*. Her previous novel is *Painted Woman*.

Novelists often complain that people keep asking them where they get their ideas from. I'm glad when I hear people ask this of other novelists because it's the question I'm always wanting to ask, although I know from experience that it's hard to say where anything begins, let alone an idea. I began my new novel, *Leaning Towards Infinity*, when a friend was visiting me. I was nursing my new baby, and my friend was struggling with a dire illness, and it moved me that he didn't talk about his illness, but mathematics. I sensed he was holding something as real and wonderful and exotic to him as my baby was to me. There'd always been two sorts of mathematics to me—the dry-chalky-sums-on-Friday-afternoon sort, and the mathematising that seems encoded in our gene pool for no obvious reason—our ability to use mathematics is way beyond anything required for survival. It's obvious that we need some basic calculating skills to tell that it's better to camp by a deeper pool than a shallow pool so we have water longer. But what about, for example, the autistic savants in Oliver Sacks' *The Man*

Who Mistook His Wife for a Hat? They were uneducable but they delighted in shouting multi-digit prime numbers at each other—a feat, as Paul Davies said, equivalent to marvellous high jumpers who leap not 6 feet off the ground, or even 60, but 600 feet. They obviously know short cuts to our cumbersome ways of calculating, but what are they doing? Are we all capable of it? Does it mean we were prepared for something more than survival?

In the past, whenever I'd encountered the argument that nothing is real, that the whole world might be a fiction or a dream, I'd say to myself: it's all right, there's mathematics. My visiting friend, to my alarm, suggested that mathematics might not be real either—that it might be a man-made edifice. But a long-held security can't be so easily stripped away. All right, I conceded, but at least numbers are real—they exist somewhere out there, perhaps in a universe of their own, a sort of numbers heaven. My friend pointed out that this was only one school of thought, the so-called Platonic school, which suggests that mathematical truth lies like an ocean around us and we explore it like scientists. This ocean of mathematical truth would exist even if there were no mathematicians at all. As John Barrow put it, Pi is really in the sky. My friend explained that mathematicians when they're working believe in this mathematical, discoverable ocean. But if you were to corner your neighbourhood mathematicians at a party they'd deny it, and say that they're only engaged in an intellectual game, playing according to formal rules. That is, it's all invented. This view is fashionable and respectable. But unfashionable Platonism is in the heart of mathematics.

This revelation sent me spinning in a life crisis, and novelists have one solution to life crises. I gave it to my heroine. She became a mathematician, backyard, amateur, not from the establishment at all, but it was still an appalling transmogrification—I knew no mathematics. I knew her quest had something to do with whether mathematics exists, whether we invent it or a third and even stranger possibility—

does it take someone to think about for it to come into being? And if we play that sort of role in the universe—well, then, the questions, you see, were becoming very large.

I had no choice. I took myself off to mathematics class, thinking that there I'd find fellow pilgrims. I had two problems. I couldn't do higher mathematics. In fact the class I had to enrol in was a remedial class. But the worse problem was that I found that mathematicians aren't interested in talking about what mathematics is—they're interested in doing it. There's a general attitude that those who can do, and it's left up to the others to talk about it. Way back, in the early years of this century, mathematicians and logicians had been embarrassed by the many logical paradoxes threatening to undermine the foundation of mathematical thought. David Hilbert, the famous mathematician said in 1900:

> The present state of affairs is intolerable. Just think, the definitions and deductive methods which everyone learns, teaches and uses in mathematics, the paragon of truth and certitude, lead to absurdities.

So Bertrand Russell and A.N. Whitehead tried to put mathematics on a logical basis. But the paradoxes defeated them. Then thirty years later Kurt Gödel brought in more confusion by showing logically that mathematics contains statements that may be true, but they're inherently unprovable.

So is mathematics a science, or a religion? I began to correspond with the physicist Paul Davies about this, but when he asked me in all kindness what question I was trying to ask, I had to admit that I didn't know enough to even formulate a question, and that, to me, is the job of a novelist—to find the right questions. I sat in libraries for years, reading mathematics journals, sometimes rigid with boredom, sometimes with my heart pounding, such as when I read about a philosopher who said that the line between two points is there before we draw it. How can it be, unless mathematics pre-exists us, part of a mystical and transcedental world? I realised as I read that mathematics depends on what were once assumptions, which were never testable. But now they're taken so much as truths that the very idea of questioning them is unintelligible. For example, the idea of proof doesn't bear too close an examination. I'd thought that mathematicians spend their time proving things. But they don't. They only show that things can be proved. A proof would need to be translated into formal language with a given list of symbols or an alphabet, then you'd write down the hypothesis of your theorem using the same symbolism, then you'd show that you can transform the hypothesis step by step, using the rules of logic till you get to the conclusion. But no mathematician does this. It'd take forever. Besides, this method goes into the realm of philosophy, into an investigation of what mathematics is about, and by then I knew what mathematicians thought of that. So a proof is an argument that convinces someone who knows the subject. It depends on what the experts think. They have to be sympathetic. Which they're likely to be if the mathematician is a respectable part of the mathematics establishment. But my heroine wasn't. Remember—she was a backyard mathematician, an amateur, an outsider. In my novel, *Leaning Towards Infinity* there's a cynical PR man who asks a mathematics professor about my backyard amateur heroine:

'You're saying there's something wrong with her work?'

The professor cries, 'Wrong? We're not discussing right and wrong like priests. In a long proof like hers, value judgements can enter. The authenticity of a proof isn't absolute, only probabilistic. If it had been known that her theorems came instead from an established mathematician, my junior wouldn't even have checked them. Symbols and operations don't have a precise meaning in mathematics, only a probabilistic one.'

'Wait a minute,' says the cynical PR man. 'You mean you lot are only probably right? So you could all be up the creek.'

I began to ask the fate of rank outsiders like my heroine. Professors of mathematics are busy people, like all of us, and are besieged several times every day by amateur mathematicians who believe they have made a discovery that could overturn mathematics. You can understand a professor's impatience. But what about the occasional genius? Occasionally one *is* discovered—for example, the Indian mathematician Ramanujan, an office clerk who sent his eccentric mathematics to three mathematical experts in 1913. Only one, G.H. Hardy, took him seriously, realising that as he read Ramanujan's letter he was rummaging through the mind of a genius. He said that Ramanujan's mathematics 'must be true, because no one would have the imagination to invent them'. In fact, Ramanujan's papers are still being plumbed for their secrets, and cosmology and computer science depend on them.

I began to realise that the whole structure of mathematics is full of loose ends, assumptions, contradictions, gaps. It's like a wild, labyrinthine cathedral designed by a mad person whose ideas on architecture occasionally come good. For example, we know very little about prime numbers, those numbers that some autistic savants understand so well.

As I read, I began to suspect that the ancient Greek acceptance of Socratic logic—and therefore our acceptance of it—owed as much to the idosyncracies of Greek politics and the magnetic personality of Socrates, as to its inherent virtue. For example, Socrates ridiculed Zeno of the Sophists, a young man who pointed out very reasonably that by the rules of Socratic logic, a swift runner like Achilles could never catch up to a tortoise who had a head start in a race, because the runner would always be halving the distance between himself and the tortoise, on and on into infinity. For two thousand years, Zeno's ideas couldn't be countered. But to the eloquent and powerful Socrates, Zeno the Sophist spoke only sophistry.

As Zeno's argument indicated, there are other possible alternatives to true and false, which is the way we think, with an allowance for areas of grey. But in ancient India, for example, you could take for granted not two, as we have, but seven possibilities—maybe something is, maybe it isn't, maybe it is but it isn't, maybe it's indeterminate, maybe it is but it's indeterminate, maybe it isn't but it's indeterminate, or may it is and it isn't and it's also indeterminate. I began to wonder if we saw things in this way, could we have a totally different way of thinking? A totally different mathematics? And would it work as well? Maybe worse. Maybe better. At least, differently. Would we see another world? Would we have a different technology? A different space travel. You see how the questions proliferate again.

It's a commonplace theory that mathematics describes the world well, even if this is only a coincidence. The rationality of science depends on mathematics. But does it describe much of the world? Are we looking down a narrow tunnel at a world defined and limited by our mathematics?

Remember Pythagoras of the famous triangle theorem? How the square on the hypotenuse equals the sum of the squares on the other two sides? He had a cult following, a mystical group who were fascinated by numbers. But oddly enough, they took a while to consider that if you have a triangle with sides of one unit long, then the side called the hypotenuse is going to be the square root of two. Eventually someone called Hippasus upset the known mathematical world of the time by asking what you were to do with such an answer which you couldn't exactly calculate. The ancient Greeks hated inexactitude. (Their word for infinity, *apeiron*, also means a used, dirty handkerchief.) His question opened up a rift between arithmetic, which could create this monster, and geometry, which couldn't measure it. It was a question so shocking, the mathematicians of the day had no choice. They drowned the questioner.

I began to ask why some subversive ideas are taken up, and some not. I was delighted to find that Morris Kline suggested in his history of mathematics, subtitled *The Growth of Uncertainty*, another more whimsical meaning of the Archimedes' principle (you remember, that a body immersed in water is buoyed up by a force equal to the weight of the water displaced). Morris Kline said that we owe to Archimedes and his bathtub the explanation of how as humans we can remain afloat, in a world of forces that threaten to submerge us.

So is mathematics a charting of something sublime, or a map of the mind, or a giant metaphor for existence, or a way some people have of getting in touch with another world? It seems to me that since we are 98 per cent chimpanzee, our most abstract ideas are mixed up with our tissue, our blood, our matted hair. Mathematical inspiration touches whatever it means to be human. It's like thinking about mathematics while you're holding a baby. There must be meeting places between mathematics and the processes of love. I wanted to write about love relationships that lean towards infinity.

This led me to consider genius as a comparative term, and to be moved at the tragedy of someone who is almost a genius—but not quite. A woman of the last generation who is both a daughter and a mother and who after early promise as a mathematics prodigy is beset by housework, drudgery and a constricting society. I had found my question at last. What would be her relationship to a daughter who could not only inherit her work, but explore it better? And if this woman, an outsider, a backyard genius, discovered a new sort of number that could question mathematics, what would happen to her in the contemporary world? Would she be ignored? Would she be celebrated? Or would she be drowned?

THE BUSINESS OF
SCIENCE

TREVOR McALLISTER

**TREVOR McALLISTER, who was born in Belfast, took
up science during the Sputnik era and now is a
research scientist with the CSIRO in Melbourne.**

In January 1957, C.P. Snow wrote his famous essay on the Two Cultures for the British periodical *New Statesman*. His thesis was that
specialisation in the education system was creating an elite class of
scientific and technical experts on the one hand and a scientifically
ignorant class of administrators on the other. He wrote at a time when
science was in the ascendant: the Atomic Age had arrived with nuclear
weapons and power stations challenging mankind with its greatest
ever example of the biblical problem of swords and ploughshares;
Crick and Watson had unravelled the molecular structure of DNA; here
in Australia, Alan Walsh had invented the atomic absorption spectro-
photometer which was to become one of our greatest technological
exports during the following three decades; a whole range of projects
in CSIRO labs were solving problems of poor soils and difficult ore
bodies for the agricultural and mining industries. To the lay observer,
science must have seemed brimful of confidence, and the yield on
government investment in research so beneficent and bountiful that

there was no room for expressions of doubt such as Snow's.

Yet Snow was of course right to air his misgivings about how nations would cope with the problems of an increasingly scientific age when most of the decision makers and media informers were scientifically illiterate. Here in the 1990s we live in an age of uncertainty. The overweening confidence of the late '50s is long gone. Funding for science is no longer an assured side benefit of government appropriation, but an annual trial of negotiation with private industry or government agency sponsors. Society regards science and technology, if it thinks of them at all, with suspicion as, at best a waste of money, at worst, a source of pollution and doomsday biological experiments. The genie of the '50s has become the orphan of the '90s.

Where did it all go wrong? Should we have listened more closely to Snow, made more effort to de-specialise ourselves as scientists, to move people with scientific training into areas of management and politics? But people with scientific training have always entered these fields. Snow himself did so. Although their numbers may not have been large, they have often been in positions of influence and power, yet they have left no legacy of scientific culture in government and management, which are still dominated by the legal, accountancy and economics professions. Would more have really been better, or was there a deeper cultural division than Snow himself realised?

It was not that we did not recognise science as a somewhat different culture which had to be accepted by mainstream society as well as by the decision makers. We did, and we're still working on it. We have science centres which popularise basic concepts, and many other programs from professional organisations which seek to explain science and the scientific effort to the public. A similar effort devoted to ethnic multiculturalism during the past decade has yielded substantial benefits in terms of social harmony in Australia. Why hasn't it done the same for science and scientists, who might themselves be considered an ethnic minority of a very special kind?

We have not asked ourselves whether Snow, having defined the problem, got the identity of the opposing cultures right. If there were conflicting cultures around science, were they really Science and Humanities, which coexist in tertiary education, and frequently combine in the same person, so that they could really be regarded as two churches of the same faith: knowledge? Haven't the genuinely inimical cultures been identified during the last decade as business and science?

Business likes to make profits, science likes to make discoveries. Discoveries don't necessarily lead to profits, and if they do, business likes to keep them confidential rather than publish them to the world, as science does. This is a fundamental conflict that can be summed up in that dreadful modern term, 'Intellectual Property'. How can anything genuinely intellectual be anyone's property? Elaborate schemes for cooperative research centres between academia, government labs and business can founder on legal disputes about intellectual property. If they don't, by the time the scientists start the first benchwork, a substantial amount of the total expense of the project can have gone on getting the intellectual property agreement right.

Legal pitfalls abound and the prospect of us descending into an American style of technological development by lawsuit is very real. This is perhaps the greatest clash of cultures, undreamt of by Snow: the adversarial nature of our legal system is quite unsuited to deal with technical and scientific questions which are subject to the Heisenberg uncertainty principle.

Business expects business plans for each year's operation. Scientific discovery and invention don't proceed according to plan. This is not a novel difficulty. There is often a similar misunderstanding between politicians and the military. Politicians want quick results from their generals so that they can hold a victory parade before they are flung out of office. They argue with generals about over-caution, then, once battle is joined, about progress not occurring according to plan.

Experienced generals know that they need a plan to give focus to an operation, but also know that battles seldom proceed according to plan. Montgomery's original plan for the Normandy campaign in 1944 is still a matter of historical controversy because of the differences between the original timetable and the actual fighting.

It's much the same in research. Knowing this, scientists don't like making detailed plans and are unhappy when forced to by managers responsible for business negotiations. How can you say what you are going to discover or develop in six months' time? If you really knew in advance, there would be no point in doing the research. Because of this difference, a great deal of insincerity occurs in the business/science relationship.

Fraught with such difficulties as these, it's hardly surprising that the science/business relationship, which is in its infancy in Australia, has come to grief on several occasions, and even ended up in the courts. Sueing a large research organisation may be a smart entrepreneurial way to make a windfall profit, but it's a damn silly way to conduct a science and business policy. Many scientists are now asking themselves whether their profession hasn't gone too far in trying to get the business dollar, and whether we can't go back to being poor but honest.

The trouble is that there is no going back. The golden era of the '50s and '60s was dead long ago, but its afterglow has lived on to illumine our hope through the '80s that such times would come again. But just as typing has become word processing, and election campaigns have become media events, with a much greater expenditure of effort for the same result as before, so has science become irretrievably involved with business, with all the inevitable elaboration and expense of conducting the relationship.

What can we do to cope with this? As in a troubled marriage, we've got to work at it. As scientists we're at a disadvantage, in that we have to play the role of anxious suitor, seeking the attention of business and convincing them that they need us. This supplicant role is not very flattering for a profession that seemed so on top as did science in 1957.

When you have reluctant parties, intermediate professions spring up to fill the negotiation gap. Lawyers of course have always fulfilled this function in human society. Now we have a rash of new specialist managers—business managers, communication managers, even, heaven forbid, intellectual property managers. These, with their inevitable coteries of deputies and assistants, are the marriage brokers of the new business/science relationship. C.P. Snow would not recognise the modern research organisation. In 1957, a CSIRO division had a chief and a divisional secretary to do all this work, to find companies to commercialise inventions, and to tie up patents with patent attorneys. The modern division has a squad of people pursuing and documenting the business dollar. Research managers no longer spend most of their time thinking about research—that has become the easy part. And the scientists at the bench? There is an uneasy sense amongst those who can recall the days of C.P. Snow, when we were in school and the first Sputnik flew, that we have become proletarianised, mere industrial fodder to be switched around or disposed of at will.

In order to encourage this pursuit of the business dollar, the government set CSIRO a target of 30 per cent external funding. University science faculties find themselves, if not with such a clear directive, nevertheless with an ongoing imperative to get external funds. Some parts of the organisation or faculty are able to meet these targets, others fall well short. So we find that two nations of scientists are created: the haves and the have-nots. A tricky policy decision is now required. Do you cross-subsidise from projects that are oversubscribed to those that are less attractive to commercial interests?

The projects that have succeeded in the external funding race naturally feel that the money is justly theirs, forgetting that they have succeeded only as part of a wider organisation whose infrastructure and cultural support system has made their activity possible. Those that did not succeed, on the other hand, may not have put enough effort into doing so. Should they be rewarded for their sloth? It is also a risk that more than 30 per cent of an organisation's effort can go into getting that 30 per cent external funding, in which case the organisation is living on its capital, and its lifetime in terms of new ideas is limited.

The external funding concept is based on the 'user pays' philosophy so beloved of the market economists who dominate government and private industry policy making. Users might justifiably complain that they have paid already in taxes, why do they have to pay again? Purists might point out that 'user pays' assumes a classical market in research. It is very doubtful if such a market exists anywhere, let alone Australia. In much research endeavour, the concept of market failure is more appropriate, and the question then becomes a matter of social, as opposed to economic, policy. 'User pays' and 'market forces' are Orwellian slogans used as a substitute for thought in determining policy.

All this, of course, has increased suspicion of managerial motives in research organisations at the very time when more trust is required all round to make the new system work, however imperfectly. It only takes one or two examples of bad or selfish management of external funding issues to run through an organisation and destroy that essential bond in scientific research which was one of the virtues of the old system. Can we survive this period of adjustment? If only the commercially successful parts of an organisation are allowed to survive and the unprofitable infrastructure of fundamental research and knowledge to disappear, that organisation will end up as mere short-term providers of consultation services—often sneeringly referred to as 'panel beating' in research circles.

In the end it comes down to the quality of the people who run this system, at all levels. Character still matters in human organisation, and people will overcome this cultural difference if there is the will to do so and the trust and skill in human relations. This means that business has to work at the relationship as well as science, and as presumably businesses who seek out research are interested in the longer rather than the shorter term, to get that longer term benefit they have to build a relationship with their researchers.

There is no long-term solution in research managers taking MBAs. That is the equivalent of what happened after Snow's article in 1957, when schools promptly started humanities classes for science students. Universities in Australia now insist on Science and Engineering students doing an Arts subject during their undergraduate studies, but we still don't get Arts students having to do a science subject—a genuine science subject that is, not History and Philosophy of Science. Business executives have to try to understand the scientific process as their contribution to the new relationship. Maybe then the ghost of Snow can be laid to rest.

THE REALITY OF
EXTINCTIONS

PETER JAMES

**PETER JAMES is a consultant in the Earth Sciences
and has written books of both fact and fiction. The
following piece is taken from *Earth In Chaos*.**

Extinction of the dinosaurs has always been a fitting topic for popular
science, particularly through its alleged link to meteorite impact. In
contrast, other extinctions have never caught the public imagination
in the same way, yet there have been equally dramatic events quite
close to our own time.

A mere 10 000 or 11 000 years ago—the traditional end of the last
Ice Age—something like 70 per cent of the large animals in North
America were wiped out. In South America, the percentage was even
greater. Mastodon, lion, sabre-tooth tiger, giant armadillo . . . all simply
disappeared from the face of these continents. They were not alone.
At much the same time, in Europe, the woolly rhino and the mammoth
became extinct; likewise the Irish deer and Irish sheep, and very
nearly the European horse. At that time, at least in Europe, man was
still living in scattered winter caves, so it does not seem logical to
blame the voracious human appetite for these disappearing acts.

In Australia, if we step back to 20 000 years ago, we come upon an extinction event which accounted for 90 per cent of the large marsupials in this country. Again, over-hunting carries no logic as an explanation. The Aborigines already had 30 000 years of experience in livestock management prior to this extinction. (Incidentally, the giant animals which lived prior to the event are remembered still in the tales of the Dreamtime. But they would no doubt be dismissed in today's world as wild exaggeration had they not been given confirmation by white palaeontologists.)

Then, at 35 000 years ago there is another catastrophe, this time for the large populations of Neanderthals living in Europe and the Middle East. Poor old Cro Magnon has traditionally been blamed for driving the Neanderthals to extinction but Cro Magnon was painting pictures in isolated caves for ten or fifteen millennia after the Neanderthals had gone: not the sort of behaviour one might expect of an aggressive, upwardly mobile subspecies. What I am suggesting is that the Neanderthals were the victims of the same sort of natural disaster which wiped out the other large mammals.

The date of the Neanderthals' demise is, incidentally, marked by the snap freezing of large animals in Siberia and Alaska. Some pretty traumatic change in climate is implied by this and it gives us one indirect clue to a possible mechanism for extinctions.

In order to pursue this theme, I would like to take up the story in more recent prehistory, and look at the millennium which ran from around 2500 to 1500 BC. This could be loosely termed the megalithic millennium, for it was during this time that the huge monuments of standing stones were built in north-west Europe. There were several episodes of megalithic activity and, in the patterns of these standing stones, we have a record—possibly the only record—of a mechanism which I believe provides us with a cause for extinctions.

The most famous of all megalithic monuments is, of course, Stonehenge. But it is not a solitary example; hundreds of stone rings are extant in Britain alone. In addition, there are huge rows of standing stones in north-west France, just as impressive as Stonehenge. The nearby Grand Menhir, now broken, was originally 320 tonnes, the largest stone ever moved by manpower. Occasionally, a megalithic society had to work without stones and chose to make long, broad excavations on chalk downs which now resemble the overgrown preparations for a modern motorway. These have been given the name Cursus.

The expenditure of energy involved in megalithic construction was enormous and we well might ask 'Why?'. Well, there has been no shortage of speculation. An early French writer suggested that the stone rows in Brittany had been used by Caesar's soldiers for tying down their tents, but the stones were put there two thousand years before Caesar came on the scene. One archaeologist suggested the Cursus excavations were for neolithic cattle droving. An Oxford academic set out to prove that the stone rings were designed to demonstrate some pre-Pythagorean principles of geometry. The astronomer Gerald Hawkins went further. His computer analysis suggested Stonehenge was a sophisticated astronomical observatory. Yet another equally competent mathematician analysed megalithic architecture as a whole and decided there was no purpose to it whatsoever.

Despite all the controversy, commonsense tells us that megalithic man did not labour so intensively for so long unless he thought he was achieving something pretty important. In historical times, we know grand works of this type have always been linked with a magical or religious theme. Megalithic man was probably no different and so we should really seek out the magic or religion of that time to help explain his monuments.

Stonehenge again gives us a lead. Here, the magic of the final stage unequivocally lies with the midsummer sunrise. Stonehenge is Britain's sun worship monument *par excellence*. Now, hundreds of other stone rings, built during the same time as Stonehenge, share more or less the same architecture. So a sun worship basis would appear a logical explanation for them, as well. Unfortunately, not very many of them point to today's midsummer sunrise. There is a scatter of directions which, of course, has been the reason for so much speculation about their purpose.

But I began to wonder: are we looking at them in the wrong way? For instance, let us assume that all the stone rings and stone rows were sun worship monuments, tied to a midsummer ceremony. Why then are the alignments so scattered? Could it be that the sun has changed position? The idea of a major precession, or Earth wobble, comes to mind.

Consider the scenario where a small disturbing force—either in-house or externally applied by a meteorite—knocks the Earth out of kilter and temporarily sets it wobbling. Most of us have seen this sort of behaviour in a spinning top. It goes from a steady spin to a spin with a wobble, then slowly returns to the state of steady spin once more. There is a difference in that the top is fixed at the south pole, but the analogy seems reasonable enough. So I wondered what would happen if the Earth went into such a state, temporary state, of wobble.

It is a simple matter to demonstrate how the position of the mid-summer sunrise would shift either north or south on the horizon, during wobble, depending whether the Earth's axis of spin was tilted more than normal towards the sun, or vice versa, on the calculated day of midsummer. Thus a megalithic monument built to face the midsummer sunrise position on any one year would become out of alignment with it the following year, or within a few years at any rate. A new monument might then be commissioned to face the new sunrise location, or the old one might be refurbished. Indeed, Stone-henge underwent major reconstruction on at least three occasions over the millennium, and it is not uncommon to find three or four stone rings in the one paddock, each facing a slightly different direction.

One has to make allowance for latitude effects on the azimuth of the midsummer sunrise, but, when I plotted the alignments of all megalithic monuments what emerged was a concentration of directions spanning today's midsummer sunrise position. A second concentration of upside down alignments also occurred, but in the sectors between these were no megalithic alignments whatsoever. In other words, the scatter of the alignments seen today is consistent with a practice of midsummer watching during a period of Earth wobble. One of the periods of major wobble seems to have been in the closing stages of the third millennium BC, a century or two before 2000 BC.

Following this smell of success I then sought other data to support the interpretation. Egypt sprang to mind as a sun-worshipping society, and one which built monuments at the start of the megalithic era. We hear so much about the perfect alignment of the pyramid of Cheops that we tend to forget some of the others. Cheops is, in fact, the only one which lines up so well with the cardinal points. Other major pyramids, both pre- and post-dating Cheops, are out by as much as 9 degrees.

Then we have later evidence. Latitude fixes made by the Greek astronomer Hipparchus, about 130 BC, are out by 4 or 5 degrees. Almost half of the extant sundials, from 300 BC to AD 300 are in the wrong latitudes today. And we have ancient eclipse recordings: numerous first-hand accounts of total solar eclipses which give us the right dates but the wrong locations. These include statements by people like Herodotus, Thucydides and Plutarch, and it is just not realistic to dismiss them, as do many scientists. Indeed, I would go so far as to suggest that the direct observations of such people are far more reliable than the back calculations of a modern academic with his computer. My alternative suggestion is that all the above maverick data fit quite neatly into a proposal of Earth wobble. So ends Part One of the story.

Part Two is this. If the Earth did undergo wobble, or fast precession, what other effects might this have besides a simple shift in the position of the midsummer sunrise?

Firstly, during wobble, the rate of spin would have to reduce slightly in accordance with the principle of conservation or angular momentum. Secondly, the shape of the Earth would be affected. We know from satellite geodesy that an extremely small precession, such as the Chandler Wobble, causes measurable changes in the shape of the Earth. Now, this is a wobble which has no effect whatsoever on our daily lives. Therefore, we must presume that a larger wobble—one which is observable to the human eye—would cause a correspondingly larger change in the shape of the Earth. Any altered geometry must, in turn, impose stress changes in the crust of the Earth: stress changes manifest as earthquake activity, possibly even by the escape of methane. However, way beyond all this would be the effect of wobble on the veneer of water that covers two-thirds of the Earth's surface. Under wobble, the oceans would be redistributed. Global sea levels would rise and fall in quite an unpredictable manner.

To put this in lay terms, Earth wobble equals ground shaking, spontaneous methane fires, violent changes in weather patterns and, above all, cataclysmic floods. We can now put in context the flood myths which come down to us from almost every country in the world and it is worth quoting from a version of one of the best known of them, recorded in the *Epic of Gilgamesh*:

The gods in the firmament were locked in death struggles. The ground was shaking, fire and tempest were raging. The gates holding back the upper ocean were torn down and floods surged across the lands to sweep away the people, filling the seas like the spawn of fish.

This is a description of humanity witnessing forces far beyond human control. It contains the ingredients of Armageddon. It is the description of an extinction event.

Which brings us back to the dinosaurs and the suggestion that they left the stage because of a large meteorite impact. Unfortunately, recent geological work reveals that this connection does not hold up. Evidence was presented at a recent conference on global catastrophes in America to show that the major extinction, which includes the dinosaurs, came not with the high iridium horizon—that is, the horizon which is taken to indicate fallout from the said impact. The major extinction came half a million years before that. And there was another one after it. This is not to deny that large impacts have occurred throughout Earth's history, but they are not necessarily extinction events. However, in both of the above extinctions, evidence does indicate massive changes in sea level. The parallel with the more recent extinction events witnessed by humanity is no coincidence.

Extinctions have always been a part of Earth history and my point is that one likely mechanism is this large and sudden change in sea level, brought on by some form of instability in the Earth's axis of spin. In the last split second of geological time, these events have been witnessed by humans. But our species, perhaps through egotism, has chosen either to disbelieve them or to endow such events with the supernatural, interpreting them as attempts by the gods to destroy mankind, not as a routine Earth hazard.

MEET NITRIC OXIDE, *SCIENCE* MAGAZINE'S 1992 MOLECULE OF THE YEAR

─────────────

ELIZABETH FINKEL

Dr ELIZABETH FINKEL is a one-time biochemist who now operates as a freelance journalist.

When I was a science student, I remember wondering whether there were in fact any great discoveries left to be made. It's a sentiment that crops up now and then, especially after major breakthroughs. In 1920, Paul Dirac discovered the laws that demystified the behaviour of the electron. It was predicted soon after that physics as we know it would be finished in six months. There were similar sentiments aired in 1966 when Nirenberg, Ochoa and Khorana cracked the genetic code. You'd have to admit that decoding the secret of life is a hard act to follow.

But for those of you wanting to make your own mark on science, don't despair. Discoveries that break new ground continue to occur. The story of nitric oxide is a case in point. If you've ever read about the gas nitric oxide it's probably been in relation to pollution. Nitric oxide is one of those gases released by car exhausts. It ends up creating photochemical smog—the scourge of cities like Los Angeles. But in the minds of physiologists worldwide, all that is in the past.

Today NO is a star performer, no less than *Science* magazine's 1992 molecule of the year. This little gas has answered long-standing questions about how blood vessels dilate, how nerves transmit messages, and learning and memory. And its clinical applications will probably give us new treatments for stroke, hypertension, Alzheimer's disease, cancer and even impotence.

It all began about six years ago. Blood vessels had long been known to produce a factor that dilated them, but no one had been able to identify this mystery substance. It went by the name of EDRF (Endothelial Cell Derived Relaxing Factor). Scientists knew that EDRF was produced by the mushy cells inside the blood vessel and then diffused out to relax the surrounding muscular band. It was a shock to the scientific community when in 1987 a number of researchers independently came to the conclusion that EDRF was probably the gas nitric oxide. A two atom gas with a three second lifespan was a most unlikely candidate for such an important biological messenger. (These days such titles go to rather more complex molecules, like prostaglandins or steroids or peptides.)

But NO as the blood vessel relaxing factor began to make more and more sense. For decades doctors have been using nitro drugs to treat angina and high blood pressure without knowing why these drugs worked. The effects of these drugs had been accidentally discovered in munitions factories. Women working with nitroglycerine had very low blood pressure. Now it's realised that compounds like nitroglycerine or sodium nitroprusside break down in the body to release nitric oxide.

Nitric oxide has pretty much revolutionised our understanding of blood vessel control. A whole new field of NO chemistry has opened up and we can probably expect a new range of drugs for treating hypertension and angina in the near future. But let's move on to a second area where NO has made a big splash.

Researchers studying nerve transmission also had a mystery to solve.

Nerve cells or neurons ferry messages around our body, from sensory organs to the brain to the spinal chord and to muscles. They are very much like wires carrying electrical signals around a circuit. Along the length of a single neuron, the signal is transmitted electrically. But where two neurons meet there is a gap, and to cross the gap the message has to be carried by a chemical called a neurotransmitter.

For many years now scientists have known that the nervous system uses several different neurotransmitters. In fact, nerves are generally named for the type of neurotransmitter they use. For example, nerves supplying skeletal muscles commonly use acetylcholine and are called cholinergic nerves, while many brain neurons use a substance called GABA and are called Gabinergic nerves. Knowing which nerves use which neurotransmitter underpins the modern use of anaesthetics, sedatives and stimulants which all work by affecting the levels of neurotransmitters.

But nerves in the intestine, lung and penis have long presented a mystery. Researchers have not been able to nail down the neurotransmitter being used. In fact, these nerves have been named for what they are not, NANC nerves, which stands for not adrenergic, not cholinergic.

Well, you guessed it, recent findings show that NANC nerves use nitric oxide as their neurotransmitter. That discovery has put a whole new category of nerve transmission into the textbooks. Researchers now speak of nitrergic nerves alongside the other categories.

Some researchers are puzzled as to how nitric oxide could possibly act as a neurotransmitter. As David Hearst of Melbourne University puts it, 'nitric oxide breaks every rule of nerve transmission'. Neurons generally go to a great deal of trouble to release their neurotransmitters with precision and speed. They package precise quantities of neurotransmitter into little torpedoes that lie ready and waiting at the nerve terminal. When detonated by a nerve signal, the torpedoes spew their contents precisely at targets on the receiving neuron.

However, nitric oxide as a neurotransmitter breaks all the rules. Once released by the transmitting neuron, the gas just diffuses out in all directions. Dr Hearst wonders how enough nitric oxide molecules could reach the receiving neuron to trigger a response. But such technicalities aside, let's proceed to yet another hotbed of nitric oxide research.

There's a third area, perhaps the most exciting of all, where NO has revolutionised scientific thinking—the brain. It may be the molecule that 'memories are made of'. Imagine the mesh of billions of entangled neurons that is our brain. That overwhelming complexity ensures that we never run out of the capacity to learn and store memories. But how are specific tasks and memories stored away in that meshwork?

When we carry out a new task, such as learning a new game, neurons scattered throughout the learning centres of the brain become activated. As we repeat the moves of the game and it becomes more familiar, connections between specific neurons strengthen, allowing the nerve signals to move along more easily—a memory circuit has been created.

It is the ability of brain neurons to change the strength of their connections, their so-called *plasticity*, that makes learning and memory possible. The process by which neurons change the strength of their connections is called *long term potentiation* (LTP). And understanding how neurons do this is the key to understanding the molecular details of the learning process—the holy grail for brain researchers.

Researchers now believe that NO has a key role to play in LTP. Consider two neurons that are part of a learning circuit. Researchers have known for some time that it is the neuron at the receiving end of the signal that initiates the strengthening process. The highly aroused neuron appears to ensure its continued association with the neuron that excited it in the first place by releasing a mystery substance referred to as the *retrograde messenger*. NO now appears likely to be that substance. Its release from an aroused neuron appears to set in train the events leading to LTP.

NO seems to fit the bill for the role of retrograde messenger very nicely. It diffuses rapidly and slips easily in and out of cell membranes. It also self-destructs within seconds, making for a very precise signal. NO as the retrograde messenger also makes sense of recent scientific reports that learning in one set of neurons appears to influence surrounding neurons. Being so diffusible, NO would be expected to influence surrounding neuron connections.

NO may yet win the dazzling title of 'the brain's memory molecule', but it may also play a deadly role—in stroke damage. Exactly what causes the massive brain cell death seen after stroke has long puzzled researchers. When brain cells are deprived of oxygen, they pour out huge quantities of the neurotransmitter glutamate. Neurons in the vicinity of this flood seem to shrivel up and die. But it has never been understood why. There were vague notions that somehow they died of overexcitement. But NO may provide a more precise explanation.

The neurotransmitter glutamate is thought to be the trigger that normally releases NO. And while a little bit of NO is good for brain power, a lot is bad. NO is toxic at high doses. In fact, macrophages, the 'Rambos' of our immune system, use it to incinerate cells. Many researchers now believe that NO may be responsible for much of stroke damage. The sequence of events seems to be: oxygen starvation leads to the pouring out of neurotransmitter, which leads to the out of control production of NO, which leads to brain damage. And that theory is supported by animal studies. The studies show that if NO inhibitors are used, more than 70 per cent of stroke damage can be prevented.

Speaking clinically, we should be hearing a lot more about NO. With vascular disease and stroke as the major killers in Western societies, it's no secret that NO research is a hot item on the R and D agendas of many a drug company. We can expect improved treatments for angina and hypertension and hopefully a long-awaited new treatment for stroke. Already at large are NO-based treatments for septic shock—

the dramatic drop in blood pressure that occurs when infections get out of control. The blood pressure drops because of all that NO being sprayed around by macrophages. NO inhibitors are now being used to treat that condition. We may also soon have a NO-based treatment for impotence. NO is the neurotransmitter used by nerves supplying the penis. With arousal, the nerves release nitric oxide which dilates the blood vessels leading to erection. If things go well for researchers at the John Hopkins Medical School in Baltimore, we may soon have a NO-releasing penile patch on the market.

NO has come a long way. Despite dubious beginnings it is now one of physiology's bright stars. It has solved mysteries in blood vessel control and nerve transmission. It may yet explain much about memory formation, stroke and who knows what else. As a recent review put it, even if only half the claims for NO are borne out, it is set to have a remarkable impact on biology and medicine.

SLEEPERS, WAKE! TECHNOLOGY AND THE EMPLOYMENT REVOLUTION

BARRY JONES

BARRY JONES is a Federal Member of Parliament, fellow of three Academies, writer and former Science Minister.

I began writing *Sleepers, Wake!* so long ago—in 1979—that it seems like another world. Heavens, there was a Coalition government! The writer of 1979 is so remote from me that I can feel quite objective about him.

The book was published in 1982 and is now in its fourth edition, twenty-first impression. On the cover the Henry Moore sculpture 'Atom Piece' has been replaced by a lugubrious photograph of me.

About forty per cent of the text is completely new. The general line of argument about the impact of technology on work remains and Jones's Eight Laws are unchanged, but the whole process has speeded up immensely and I am now astonished by my own moderation. The transition to a post-industrial or information society in Australia has largely occurred—without the benefit of public or political discussion of what has happened, or why, identifying winners and losers, and adopting appropriate policy responses.

Australia is essentially an 'information society', but a rather passive one. Forty per cent of workers are now essentially symbolic analysts. The central element of information or knowledge work is the generation, manipulation, storage, retrieval and application of *symbols*—words, numbers, sounds, images—or *symbolic objects*—banknotes, cheques, letters, certificates, printouts, photographs, film, invoices. Information products can be reduced to signals, sent through the air or along a wire and reconstituted at the other end. Industries such as film, music, entertainment, media are among the world's most powerful.

There has been a completely inadequate Australian policy response on information issues, marked by poor coordination, intensive fragmentation between Departments and suspicion between the major stakeholders.

EMPLOYMENT REVOLUTION

1 Living longer: working less, rethinking time use value The development of the 'Third Age' is a new phenomenon in demography. About two million people in Australia are likely to remain physically active for more than twenty years after retirement. In barely thirty years, the fifty-year working lifetime for many males has fallen to thirty-five years. Phil Ruthven of Ibis Consulting, Melbourne, argues that a working lifetime of 80 000 hours has been standard since 1800—the quantum is constant, only the distribution of effort has changed. By the year 2000, time actually spent on the job in paid work (excluding sleeping, leisure and commuting) is likely to contract to 12 per cent of a lifetime. He also estimates that personal involvement in or exposure to media, news and computing will soon exceed the time involved in paid work, if it has not already done so.

2 Gender In 1964 the male–female ratio in the labour force was

71:29. By 1995 it was 58:42. Improved contraception was a major cause. (The pill has been easily the most important technological factor in employment changes.) There has been a striking increase in part-time work, some by choice, many from necessity, and women dominate this sector. Between 1978 and 1995 part-time jobs increased by 107 per cent. The value of unpaid work (largely domestic, performed by women) in Australia has been estimated at $283 billion annually by Duncan Ironmonger's Household Research Unit at Melbourne University, confirming the importance of my 'Quinary' sector. It is necessary to reject the 'lump of labour' theory, the idea that there is a fixed quantum of work and that increased female employment caused job displacement for men. There is no evidence to support this.

3 Decline of the blue-collar worker The American social philosopher Peter F. Drucker has argued that 'No class has ever risen faster than the blue collar worker. And no class in history has ever fallen faster.' There have been dramatic changes in the proportion of blue collar–white collar workers: blue collars fell from 51.6 per cent in Australia in 1947 to 35.5 per cent in 1994, largely due to the decline in male work and the rise of female. There is extreme difficulty in placing the unskilled unemployed. Workers used to be referred to as 'hands' ('backs' might have been as appropriate), but jobs requiring physical strength are now in terminal decline.

4 End of 'One job for life'? Lifetime employment in a single type of work is likely to disappear and be replaced by 'modular work', involving several occupational changes in a reduced working life. There has been a sharp fall in employment opportunities for people *under* 20 and *over* 55.

We need to reconceptualise work which has always been one of the 'twin pillars' of self-definition. ('Who am I?') The family was the second pillar. In Australia and some other countries (Argentina, New Zealand, South Africa) sport may be regarded as a 'third pillar'.

Between 1978 and 1995, full-time jobs increased by 20 per cent.

5 *Differentiation* Peter Drucker asserts that the emerging post-industrial society is 'the first in which not everybody does the same work . . . This is far more than a social change. It is a change in the human condition'. Our ancestors were engaged as hunters, gatherers or home-makers—no occupational choice there. With subsistence agriculture, the entire labour force worked at ploughing, planting and harvesting at the same time. With repetitive mass production, millions worked at producing identical products at a central place and they were ruled by the clock. ('We clock on at 0845 and clock off at 1706.') But in a knowledge society, having a hundred or a thousand people performing the same task would be pointless. A hundred or a thousand people can and must create a hundred and a thousand different types of production, highly individualised. People will make their own work. It will depend less on being a servant to a master. Knowledge workers themselves are, Drucker says, already the leading (not ruling!) class of the knowledge society. This will inevitably change the way in which trade unions operate.

A central element in the Industrial Revolution was Eli Whitney's development of the theory and practice of standardised, inter-changeable components. A corollary was the theory and practice of standardised, interchangeable jobs. With the decline and fall of manufacturing as a dominant employer, undifferentiated work becomes rare.

6 *Hierarchy* The command hierarchy has flattened out and may in time disappear. Management structures now have fewer layers, greater flexibility, less authoritarianism; away from 'Fordism', with more decision making on the production line. Job design is changing. Work is less centralised, more outsourced.

7 *Participation rate* Nearly 64 per cent of people aged fifteen years and over are in the labour force in Australia, far higher than during 'the golden age of full employment' (1945–74). In the age

cohort of twenty to fifty-four years, 90 per cent of males and 70.4 per cent of females were in the labour force (including unemployed), a figure of 80.7 per cent for all persons. Of those *in work* in that cohort, 84 per cent were male, 65.8 per cent female: 74.9 per cent for all persons. Australia is experiencing the unprecedented phenomenon of high *employment* and high *unemployment* simultaneously. This apparent contradiction occurs because males who were traditionally *in* work are now *out* of it, and females traditionally *out* are now *in*. This phenomenon is broadly characteristic of most OECD countries. It is no consolation for the unemployed, however, especially unskilled and semi-skilled workers.

8 Location–region–class Some traditional working-class or rural electorates find themselves in a time warp where the labour force is still dominated by mainstream employment unchanged from the 1930s, '40s and '50s. It is easy to see why 1950 jobs are under threat— because the world of the 1990s is not looking for 1950s skills. These areas lack the skill base or the investment levels needed to make an easy transition to the world of work of the 1990s. Transition from a 1950s work situation (with 1950s skills) to one matching the 1990s is not merely difficult: it may be impossible.

For an accurate picture of unemployment regionally and sectorally, the government would have to publish a detailed map to indicate the specific location of types of work which are developing and those in decline. It would be even more illuminating, if somewhat brutal, to mark with flags those areas which are dominated by jobs which were characteristic of the 1950s, those characteristic of the 1960s, the 1970s and those thereafter.

The Liberal federal electorate of Kooyong would be marked by a flag indicating 1980s and 1990s-type jobs characteristic of a post-industrial society, dependent on high levels of education, high income levels, high participation by women, and low unemployment.

Australia's registered unemployment rate of 8.6 per cent is not evenly spread across the nation. Aggregated statistics can be very misleading: only disaggregated figures reveal the full impact of regional unemployment.

9 *From 'comparative advantage' to 'competitive advantage': the decline of resources* Australia is seriously disadvantaged by the 'inventory problem', lack of brand name goods which are high in added value and have international reputation. Historically, we have had excessive dependence on high volume production, low in unit value. We measure the value of our exports in tonnes: Singapore measures its in grams. We worry a great deal about micro-economic reforms on the wharves, but miss the more important question: 'Which smart products are now exported by ship?' Australia has been very slow to take up Michael Porter's argument in *The Competitive Advantage of Nations* (1990) that the Ricardian notion of comparative advantage (which reinforces the conservative view that we have no economic prospects outside food, fibres and minerals) is now being replaced by competitive advantage, where a small country such as Finland is able to take on the United States in specialities such as mobile telephones (Nokia) and medical assay equipment (Kone).

10 *Liberty v Security* For 150 years, the labour movement's aim generally was to reduce work, whether measured in lifetimes, years, weeks, days or hours. Since technology made sharp reductions possible, there has been a change in direction. Some elements of the labour movement now talk of maintaining or even increasing total labour input, a dramatic reversal of Marx' endorsement in his *Grundrisse* (Notebooks IV and VII) of words in a pamphlet (1821) by an anonymous English Ricardian socialist: 'The first indication of real national wealth and prosperity is that people can work less . . . [W]ealth is liberty—liberty to seek recreation—liberty to enjoy life—liberty to improve the mind: it is *disposable time* and nothing more.'

Marx dismissed the idea that production and wealth creation could be ends in themselves. His words now appear very timely: 'Thus the old view [in antiquity], in which the human being appears as the aim of production regardless of his limited national, religious and political character, seems to be very lofty when contrasted to the modern world, in which production appears as the aim of mankind and wealth as the aim of production.' The Prince of Wales, although not a Marxist, takes the same view.

Within the political and industrial labour movement there are two partisan views on this issue—'the party of liberty', which welcomes the idea of more disposable time and diversified activity, and 'the party of security', which wants to maintain existing working patterns indefinitely. Both 'liberty' and 'security' are ultimately contradictory in their effect. The libertarians quote the French socialist writer André Gorz (and even *Sleepers, Wake!*) with approval, while securitarians reflect a prevailing peer group view ('My father was a logger, and so am I, and I expect my son to be one too'). Are the two views reconcilable?

Clearly work is, for most people, not just a source of income, not only a means to an end (security), but increasingly an end in itself—a certification of competence, of being wanted, of membership in a social group, enabling people to avoid those nagging questions about time use and the self-setting of goals. ('If we didn't work, what would we do with ourselves?')

COSMOLOGY, TELEOLOGY AND DANISH GRANDMOTHERS

JOE WOLFE

JOE WOLFE is an Associate Professor in the School of Physics at the University of New South Wales.

Some cosmologists, including Alfred Wallace, Freeman Dyson and Paul Davies, have formed the opinion that, in the words of Fred Hoyle, 'the universe is a put-up job'. They are expressing their marvel that the values of its constants and the forms of its laws are just those which allow such phenomena as the formation of planets, complex chemistry, life and intelligence. Some of them—including Paul Davies—go further than this. They argue that the laws of the universe were somehow legislated with purpose so that planets, chemistry and life could develop. Does cosmology tell us—to use a line of Stephen Hawking's and the title of Davies' book—about 'the mind of God'? The argument that nature shows evidence of purpose is called teleology.

Cosmology and teleology have changed in this century as a result of relativity and quantum mechanics. Previously, classical physicists such as Newton saw both the universe itself, and the laws according to which it evolves, as being the work of a God who, as it were, wrote the rules, built the machine and set it running. Indeed, many classical

58

physicists regarded the search to understand the laws of the universe as a quest to discover God's master plan. Modern cosmologists, however, don't require a god or gods to create the universe: in their cosmology the universe itself—mass, time and space—all appear together in accordance with the laws of quantum mechanics. The largest role that modern physics leaves to a god or gods is that of deciding which laws the universe will obey, and this is the area into which teleology has moved.

Wallace, Hoyle, Dyson and others have made the point that even slight changes in some values of fundamental or cosmological constants, or even in the laws of physics themselves, would imply a universe in which life as we know it would not exist. Here are a few examples: If the universe were much less dense, then stars and planets might not form. If the universe were much more dense, then it would have stopped expanding and contracted back into a hot big crunch long ago, possibly before any supernova had had time to generate the elements needed for life. What if the laws of physics were different? If the strong nuclear force were much weaker than it is, then the electrostatic repulsion between protons would prevent the formation of large nuclei—hydrogen might be the only element. If gravity were different, or if the geometry of space-time were different, then stars might not form or planets might not have stable orbits.

Physicists usually ask, 'What are the laws of nature?' But we also ask, 'Why are the laws as they are?' Could they have been otherwise? Is there anything inevitable or preordained about the actual laws of the universe? Stephen Hawking, in his popular book *A Brief History of Time*, poses these questions, but is somewhat equivocal in answering them. His casual line about 'the mind of God' may be a metaphor. The use of the word God as a metaphor for the laws of physics has a distinguished history: Einstein used the famous phrase 'God does not play dice' as his way of saying 'The universe is not probabilistic'.

Paul Davies goes further than this: he sees a 'sort of purpose in the universe' and argues that conscious, intelligent beings are somehow 'central to the universe'—that the laws of physics are the way they are *in order* that consciousness and intelligence may develop.

This is the point that I want to dispute. I shan't argue about whether there is or isn't a divine legislator, or whether the universe is purposeful, and I shan't express a view on the origin of the laws of physics. I shall only point out the logical fallacy in teleological cosmology—the flaw in the argument for purpose in the universe.

I first wondered about purpose and contingency in the universe when I was about seven, following a discussion with my grandmother. Grandma didn't mention cosmology: rather, she told me the story of the circumstances that took her from her native Denmark to settle in Australia. (I found out later that she embellished the account enormously for dramatic effect, but that's another story.) What set me thinking was the marvellous observation that if she hadn't come all the way from Denmark, or if Grand-dad hadn't come from Germany, or if any of my various ancestors had made slightly different decisions, I would not be here. The idea that we might not have been here is something that I suppose everybody wonders about—it's one of the capital BQ Big Questions. So, at an early age, I marvelled at the chain of very slim probabilities which had led to my existence.

In spite of this marvel, I was never quite so egocentric as to imagine that my various ancestors had all decided to leave their various homelands and migrate to Australia just so that they could meet and have kids who would meet and have me! You see, even as a seven year old I think that I understood something important about probability: it changes when the event happens. Let me explain by example. The probability that the next coin I toss will be heads is 50 per cent. The probability that the last one I tossed was heads is (as it happens) zero—no calculation or theory is necessary: I can see the platypus and not Ms Windsor. I toss it twenty times and get t,t,h,h,h,t,t,t,h,t,h,t,t,t,h,h,t,t,h,t. The chances of that particular sequence (of twenty heads and tails) were about one in a million before I did it, but now it has happened and the probability is one. If I had tossed differently, then I could have produced a different series, also with a prior probability of one in a million.

If the conditions of the early universe had been such that stars never condensed, or if the strong force didn't exist and the periodic table had only one entry, or if anything else had been slightly different, then we wouldn't be here—whatever 'here' might mean in such a context. But it makes little sense to talk about the universe being improbable after the event. The *conditional* probability of the universe being as it is, *given the existence of these particular human cosmologists to marvel at it*, that conditional probability is either exactly one or very very close.

I hope the parallels with coin tossing are obvious: the chances of any one particular head–tail sequence is small, and if I toss twenty coins again there is only a one-in-a-million chance that I would get the same series again. But this does not make the first sequence profoundly special: it is special only in the sense that it is the one that happened. Analogously, if we were somehow to start cosmic history over again from a big bang, the chances that we would get the same phenomena or objects, or even phenomena or objects of the same sort, may be very small. But does that make the universe special? The universe does have planets, chemistry, life and us: it is special in the sense that it has us in it, but that of course is a given in this problem because we are here talking about it.

Now I can foresee an objection from the teleologists. They might say 'Well what if your twenty coin tosses had been all heads? Wouldn't you then be surprised? Wouldn't you then look to see if someone had fixed the coin?' Well the answers are 'yes' and 'yes'. But a sequence of heads is not a good analogy to a universe which contains us. There is a way of defining something that is at least subjectively special about a sequence of all heads, using the concept of algorithmic entropy developed by Kolmogorov and Chaikin. Essentially it says that some sequences are simpler than others because an algorithm exists for reproducing them from a smaller quantity of information.

But what is comparably simple about the universe? In what way is the universe special? The teleologists would say that it is special because it allows planets, life, intelligence (and even cosmology) to exist. But that is not a small conditional probability: there is nothing improbable about that given that we—planet-based, intelligent life-forms—*are* here. If the universe were different then something else would be here—that something might not include planets, life or intelligence as we know it.

This position is close to what is called the weak anthropic principle. Stephen Hawking puts it nicely in his book. 'Intelligent beings,' he says, 'should not be surprised if they observe that their locality in the universe satisfies the conditions that are necessary for their existence.' He's right of course. But the anthropic principle can, with the same logic, be applied to the laws of physics themselves. One can equally state that: 'Intelligent beings should not be surprised if the laws of physics are consistent with the existence of intelligent beings.'

It is occasionly alleged that the anthropic principle 'explains' the nature of the universe. We exist, and for us to exist the universe must be as it is, and our existence is said, by some, to 'explain' the nature of the universe. In fairness it should be said that this strong version of the anthropic principle is perhaps more often raised as a straw man by its opponents who then proceed to knock it down. But if the anthropic principle is said to be an 'explanation', it is not an explanation in the usual sense in which scientists use the word. My grandparent analogy is helpful here: if my grandmother had not come to Australia I would not exist, but my existence does not *explain* why she came to Australia—or at least it is not an explanation in the usual sense. (As to the actual explanation of her migration, I'm not sure which of my grandma's stories to believe on this, but I'm certain that she did not say: 'I'll go to Australia so that I can meet Ferdinand and marry him and give birth to May who will marry Jim and produce Joe'.)

So let's get back to teleological cosmology. Here is what Paul Davies said recently.

> The laws of physics didn't have to be as they are—they could have been otherwise . . . there's no logical compulsion why things have to be the way they are. So this inevitably begs the question: Is there anything special about the actual laws of the universe? Well the answer is yes: far from being any old ragbag of laws, the actual laws seem to be remarkably ingenious—one might even say contrived in their particular form. Not only do the laws permit a universe to come into being spontaneously—as it were create itself—they also permit it to be self-organising.

Davies then goes on to argue that 'the universe as a whole displays a sort of purpose', that 'consciousness is a fundamental rather than an incidental feature of the universe' and that we (that is, conscious beings) 'are central, not incidental to the universe'.

Well I agree with him about one thing: his argument begs the question. If the laws of physics did not allow the universe to come into existence, or if they did not allow any of the organisation that is essential to life, Paul Davies would not be here to comment on how contrived those very laws were, or to argue that those laws must have been chosen so as to allow a universe to exist and to contain a conscious being such as Paul Davies.

The history of cosmology seems to be a story of humans conquering our vanity: cosmologists in the Western tradition had to discover that the Mediterranean was *not* the centre of the world, that the world was not the centre of the solar system, and that the sun was not the centre of the galaxy nor the galaxy the centre of the universe. This planet, this sun and this galaxy are all special—for us—in that they support us and that we, being here, observe them. They are not particularly special in any other way. The laws of nature are special in the same sense—that they support us and that we, being here, can observe them. They are not particularly special in any other way.

Teleology is not new of course: Alfred Wallace presented a cosmological version of it in 1903. Nor is my objection new: 200 years ago Immanuel Kant argued in a similar way to show the falsity of the teleological argument for creation, and Voltaire gave the Panglosses of the world a hard time in his book *Candide*. So today it's unnecessary to refute the speculation that the universe was *created* like this deliberately so that intelligent life could develop. I have just used similar logic to show the flaw in the argument that the *laws* of the universe were somehow deliberately legislated in order to allow, or even to oblige, life and consciousness to develop.

Still, as it seems that there are cosmologists who seriously propose this position, I'd be interested to hear whether they have similarly egocentric views on the actions of their grandmothers.

ALL US APES

COLIN GROVES

COLIN GROVES is a Reader in the Department of Archaeology and Anthropology at the Australian National University. His research interests are the classification and evolution of primates and other mammals.

Even some scientists still tend to draw a line: there are humans, and then there are 'animals'. This is curious, because it was as long ago as 1863, when Thomas Huxley published 'Man's Place in Nature', that this became a view that was no longer possible to sustain. Our closest living relative is the chimpanzee; the chimpanzee's closest living relative is not the gorilla, not the orang-utan, but us. And we are *very* close; we and the chimpanzee share 98.6 per cent of our DNA. Although chimpanzees, gorillas and orang-utans are commonly lumped together as Great Apes, they have nothing in common with each other that they do not share with us. We too are Great Apes.

What we seem to mean when we make a 'human v animal' distinction is that our species, the human species, has certain qualities of *mind* that are quite outside those seen in any other member of the animal kingdom. But this notion too is badly out of date—non-human Great Apes share many of the mental faculties we used to imagine as specifically human. They score very highly on conventional mental tests, including multistep logical calculation; they recognise themselves in mirrors; they have proved capable of language-like communication; they exhibit culture-like transmission of behaviour under natural conditions; they show the ability to engage in pretend play; they scheme, plan ahead, try to read each others' minds. And chimpanzees, being closest to us, share most with us; including, I'm sorry to say, the ability to engage in planned, cooperative warfare.

Now, in most of these characteristics they are not the equal of the *average* human being, but don't forget that profoundly intellectually disabled people are still human. (Our law-makers apparently did— only in 1971 did the United Nations General Assembly adopt a Declaration on the Rights of Mentally Retarded Persons; up until then, even the mildly intellectually handicapped were not unambiguously protected under international law.) Normal non-human Great Apes can do things that some humans cannot. For example, autistic people cannot pretend, nor can they see the world from another individual's point of view. Profoundly mentally retarded human beings have little or no language, and cannot recognise their own images in mirrors. Human children, of course, are born without these abilities, and acquire them bit by bit with maturity.

A recent book, *The Great Ape Project*, edited by Paola Cavalieri and Peter Singer, has made the claim that, because there is no essential, consistent, cognitive difference between humans (taken as a whole) and other Great Apes there can be no essential moral difference. All Great Apes, human and non-human, under this argument, deserve equality of treatment, which involves the Right to Life, the Protection of Individual Liberty, and the Prohibition of Torture. The core of the argument is put, in a chapter in the book, by the Finnish philosophers Häyry and Häyry, in the form of four propositions and two conclusions, thus:

P1 Beings who are equal in the moral sense ought to be treated equally.

P2 Beings are equal in the moral sense if their mental capacities and emotional lives are roughly at the same level.

P3 The mental capacities and emotional lives of human beings and other Great Apes are roughly at the same level.

C1 Therefore, human beings and other Great Apes ought to be treated equally.

P4 Human beings ought not to be killed, imprisoned or tortured unless certain specific conditions prevail.

C2 Therefore, other Great Apes ought not to be killed, imprisoned or tortured unless the same specific conditions prevail.

(They explain that, of course, no conditions would appear to justify torture; self-defence (or euthanasia?) might justify killing, and protection of society might justify imprisonment.)

Now, in order for their rights to be covered by law, non-human Great Apes would have to be considered *persons*. Is this possible? For the philosopher, personhood incorporates rationality and self-consciousness, and generally some further stipulation such as that a person is capable of reciprocity, and capable of treating us as members of the same moral community. In the philosophical sense, then, there seems no question: chimpanzees, gorillas and orang-utans are persons. In terms of the law, it is not out of the question either that they could be considered persons; already a person does not necessarily have to be human: for example, corporations are persons, with rights to sue, to hold property, and so on. The category of persons who are not regarded as mentally competent are legally assigned guardians who take action on their behalf, and are not considered criminally liable; presumably this is the category to which non-human Great Apes would be assigned.

How far beyond the Great Apes can 'personhood' be claimed? Not, at any rate, to monkeys, which have *not* shown the ability to recognise themselves in mirrors, to exhibit language-like skills, to engage in pretend-play, and so on. Persons they are not—this does not imply, of course, that they do not have a right to be treated with consideration and decency. Outside the primates there seems even less approach to the 'personhood' criteria; except possibly in cetaceans (such as dolphins), but we need to know much more about them than we do at present. It does seem plausible, in fact, that these abilities we have spoken of come more or less as a package; it may be significant that they seem to emerge within a restricted period of time (about eighteen months to four years) in human children, though not all together (early signs of language first, social attribution last).

Are adult non-human Great Apes, then, cognitively equivalent to human children at about four years of age? Yes and no. An adult chimpanzee, unlike a human infant, is a self-functioning entity; but unlike a human infant, a chimpanzee will develop no further. Or, *little* further: a famous pygmy chimpanzee, Kanzi, who lives at a Primate Centre at Atlanta in the United States, was the first (and is not the last) who learned spontaneously—he was not taught—to use linguistic symbols, to understand human language and follow complicated instructions, to make stone tools, and even to roast marshmallows and blow on them to cool them . . . and that should warn us not to underestimate non-human Great Apes!

Much the same is relevant for the comparison to intellectually handicapped people. It is claimed that Koko the gorilla at forty-three to sixty-five months of age scored between seventy-one and ninety-two IQ points; while I'm sure the standards used for human children are not closely applicable to the more rapidly growing gorilla, even an IQ in the seventies would put Koko somewhere in the merely 'mildly retarded' category.

Can we really argue for all Great Apes—humans, chimpanzees, gorillas and orang-utans—to be *moral* equals, deserving of equal treatment, persons in the philosophical and legal sense? I can see no alternative. If we take human rights, in their fullest sense, as axiomatic, then the sort of criteria we use cannot logically be reorganised in any way to exclude other Great Apes.

Reaction to the proposals put forward in *The Great Ape Project* has been mixed, but I found only one review that was firmly hostile—Miranda Stevenson, of Edinburgh Zoo. She thinks that the whole philosophy behind the idea is a product of the European tradition, and hardly touches base with peoples or conditions in habitat countries. The problems besetting non-human Great Apes, she says, are those of conservation; every day gorillas are killed for food, orang-utans are captured for pets, their forests are destroyed for timber or for agriculture to feed growing human populations. What price the Right to Freedom?

This much, of course, is absolutely correct. It is perfectly justifed to abhor the use of chimpanzees in invasive and potentially disabling biomedical experiments, and to be disgusted by the substandard housing of non-human Great Apes in zoos and laboratories: Miranda Stevenson, like the contributors to the book, deplores these things, but can one go on to demand their 'right to immediate release'? 'Release them where', she asks, 'to the disappearing wild?'

To criticise *The Great Ape Project* for not dealing with conservation issues is, one of my colleagues has suggested, 'a bit like condemning Amnesty International on the grounds that only a few hundreds, at most thousands, of people are tortured every year while far more die from malaria and schistosomiasis'. Is it really true that a literal application of the principles, specifically the Protection of Individual Liberty, would lead to the extinction of all the non-human species? But one contributor to *The Great Ape Project*, an American professor of law, Gary Francione, points out that persons held to be mentally incompetent in some way are awarded guardians, who 'safeguard their interests and rights'; as in the case of human wards, a condition of less than total liberty would be the usual result. It is up to such guardians to ensure that the conditions of their wards so approach the liberty ideal that their rights are not compromised; if they do not do so, then, just as in the case of guardians who abuse the rights of human charges, their legal guardianship can be taken away. In other words, release of non-human Great Apes back into the wild is against their interests; it is incumbent upon us to find a way in which we can take the ones presently in labs and in poor zoo conditions and lodge them in facilities that do not compromise their comfort or their dignity as persons.

What of the criticism that the underlying philosophy of *The Great Ape Project* is that of a purely Western tradition, and is inapplicable to people in habitat countries? Such a criticism misses the point that Western philosophical traditions underpin all of international law; if it were not globally acceptable, there would be no such thing as human rights. Of course, over huge areas of the world, there *is* no such thing as human rights; a situation which is as unacceptable to Africans and Asians as it is to those who are the European philosophical tradition's direct heirs. We may have little influence over the human rights situation in places outside our jurisdiction, though it is incumbent upon us to try; similarly, we will be able to promote the rights of non-human Great Apes with confidence only within our own jurisdiction, though again we should try to extend our influence beyond those boundaries.

We will have to rethink the way we keep chimpanzees, gorillas and orang-utans in zoos; not necessarily *that* we keep them, but the way we do so. We will have to rethink the process of rehabilitating orphan chimpanzees and orang-utans into the wild; watching them, I would say that, by and large, they don't want to go! It is obviously just not acceptable to keep chimpanzees in laboratories. It is very clearly not acceptable to use chimpanzees for invasive and potentially disabling or terminal biomedical procedures; this is perhaps the aspect of *The Great Ape Project* that achieves the widest measure of acclamation—even among some members of the biomedical research community, some of whom have done it once, couldn't stomach it, and don't want it to happen any more. And more benign experiments? The testing of hepatitis vaccines on chimpanzees has never harmed any—yet!—so does this mean it is all right to do it? Even this may have to be rethought: it has been put to me by a colleague, the primatologist Joe Erwin, that there are *fewer* experiments one can perform on chimpanzees than on most humans, because they cannot give their informed consent. It is not for nothing that, in human experimentation, we insist that the subjects' consent be *informed*. Think about it.

THE NOBLE CRAP

BERND G. LOTTERMOSER

Dr BERND G. LOTTERMOSER, who works as a geology lecturer at James Cook University, received the 1995 Michael Daley Award for excellence in reporting science issues for this piece.

We all do it and we do it several times a day. Humans excrete solids and liquids.

Human excreta are commonly flushed in a system of toilets and underground pipes to sewage treatment works. I would like to take you on a journey down the toilet following your disposed of personal waste. Once through the U-bend you encounter a vile stench. The sewer pipe joins those from the kitchen, the laundry and the bathroom. The wastewater now contains food residues, shampoos, cosmetics, toothpastes, detergents and cleaning agents. Travelling downstream, the tight underground pipe widens as your neighbours contribute their smelly waste. The sewage volume increases from a little trickle to a small creek. The air is warm and humid and there is a steady flow of human excreta and food. This is an excellent breeding ground for bacteria, viruses, parasites and rats.

The sewer pipes are covered by layers of sickly slime which contain large populations and microorganisms. These microorganisms start to break down the human excrements into less complex carbohydrates, thereby generating gases like hydrogen sulphide and methane.

Along the way, oils, grease, big bits like condoms, tampons and disposable nappies are joined by a rich cocktail of toxic heavy metals and a galaxy of chemicals flowing from the drains of industry. Not all pollutants in the sewerage system are industry derived. On average 30 per cent of all heavy metals derive from household sewage such as excrements, shampoos and cleaning agents. Items you dispose of down the drain.

The underground stream, a very potent mix, has now swollen to a torrent of raw sewage. The annual relief of Australia results in one cubic kilometre of raw sewage, a volume large enough to fill Sydney Harbour.

Finally, after travelling a few hours underground you have come back to daylight again. You arrive at the sewage treatment plant. In the sewage works, microorganisms actively digest dissolved and suspended particles. During treatment, sludges rich in organic matter are extracted and effluent with low concentrations of pollutants and microorganisms is released back into the natural water cycle, into streams, lakes and oceans.

These mountains of treated excreta are growing steadily as Australians produce 1000 tonnes of sludge every day. The sludge is disposed of as fertiliser and soil conditioner on agricultural land and forests, as is being done in Melbourne. In Adelaide and Wollongong, new inventive disposal efforts use the sludge for brick manufacture or oil production. However, many cities and towns dump their sludge in landfills or stockpile the residues for decades. In Sydney and Newcastle, the wastewater—and quite often the sludge, too—is flushed away out of our lives and dumped into the ocean.

Uncontrolled release of sewage into the environment may cause infections, hepatitis and cholera to humans and toxicity to animals and plants with effects to the human food chain. Sewage sludges may contain elevated concentrations of heavy metals and organic pollutants such as pesticides, phenol, furans, dioxins, and PCBs. This is especially the case if sewage derives from industrialised or heavily populated areas. Because of the possible impact on human health and the environment, human excrement and sewage sludge are regarded as waste.

However, recent undeterred (under turd) research has highlighted the more noble aspects of sewage. Sewage sludges are rich in gold, platinum and palladium: noble metals with a very high commercial value.

Rural towns and metropolitan cities like Melbourne possess sludges with significant gold contents. Old gold-mining towns like Stawell produce sewage rich in gold. Golden sewage cannot be claimed to be another tourist attraction or part of the national identity and unique to Australia. Cities such as San Francisco, Toronto or Berlin generate sewage exceptionally rich in gold. These contents are significant. The sludges possess similar or even higher gold concentrations than ore deposits currently being mined for gold in this country.

Where does the gold come from? Clearly there are not kilograms of wedding rings or gold teeth being thrown down the toilet. One of the ultimate sources of gold is exceedingly small concentrations within the drinking water. Also, if you are wearing gold jewellery during dishwashing and showering, its abrasion will add gold to the wastewater. Significant amounts originate from industrial effluents such as dental practices, the electronics industry and jewellery manufacture.

Humans are also contributing to the gold production. Reference Man, a convenient fiction of the United Nations supposed to weigh 70 kilograms, is assumed to eat 750 grams of dry matter and drink 2 litres of water per day. Normal sober adults are in a steady state in respect to elemental inputs and outputs and this results in the continuous excretion of solids and liquids. His or her excretion averages 50 grams of dry faeces and 1 litre of urine per day. The human diet contains gold in trace amounts and after food digestion most of the gold is excreted. Gold excretion in the form of faeces and urine is of major importance compared to sweat and hair loss.

Gold compounds used in medicine for the therapy of arthritis and cancer also contribute to the gold in sewerage. A portion of the administered gold drug remains within the patients' bodies. However, a significant amount of the gold is excreted following treatment and these gold-rich excreta end up in the sewerage system.

The metal content of sewage varies among other factors with the population lifestyle. People frequently exposed to noble metals excrete more gold uian others. Further research has to show whether the rich and yuppy suburbs, Toorak in Melbourne or Vaucluse in Sydney, also produce exceptionally noble excrements. However, the world population is urinating only 100 kilograms of gold each year; an exceedingly small amount compared to 100 tonnes of gold accumulating in sewage worldwide.

People should not start pegging their septic tanks in the backyard in the hope to find another Kalgurli orebody. The gold enrichment of sewage occurs in the extensive underground sewer pipes carrying the sewage to the treatment plants and it is caused by the enormous volume of wastewater flowing through the sewers. The daily relief of Melbourne results in over 1000 million litres of wastewater or in over 10 000 litres of raw sewage every second. During the three to four-hour journey along the sewerage system, gold and other metals are continuously being precipitated from the wastewaters onto the floating and suspended solids. The raw sewage eventually arrives at the treatment plant and the particles are rich in gold. Melbourne wastewaters accumulate sixty kilograms of gold each year, worth more than half a million dollars.

Sydney residents might be excited to hear that they are responsible for the accumulation of tonnes of gold off-shore. Unfortunately, the gold did not accumulate off-shore in Swiss bank accounts. It is gold present in the sediments off the coast of Sydney.

Every day Sydney-siders pour 1300 million litres of wastewater into the Pacific Ocean right into the feeding ground of marine life and treat the coastal waters as the last garbage bin. Ocean sediments near sewage outlets, like those of the city of Athens or Los Angeles, are known to be rich in gold. The dumping of sewage into our oceans produces man-made gold deposits. Every year over one million tonnes of metals, 5000 tonnes of silver, 100 tonnes of gold and 80 tonnes of palladium accumulate in sewage worldwide.

Why is sewage not mined for metals? Gold in sewage is not a flash in the pan. The gold contents of many sludges are ore grade. Metals of geological ores are mined, extracted and used for industrial products to keep our standard of living, whereas metals in sewage are literally wasted, dumped on land or at sea, or even released to the environment.

Sewage sludges contain other valuable constituents such as phosphate, nitrogen, fibre, starch, mineral oil, sugar and proteins. Also they are rich in a wide range of vitamins, especially in vitamin B12. Protein and fat concentrations are so high that their extraction has been considered for the manufacturing of soap.

Our effluent society cannot afford to waste raw materials and sewage should not be regarded as waste but as a secondary resource for metals and nutrients for plant growth. The production of excrements is secured as long as the human race exists; excreta are one of the few renewable and thus very attractive resources on our planet.

INDONESIA'S FOREST

PROPAGANDA

CLIVE HAMILTON

Dr CLIVE HAMILTON is Executive Director of The Australia Institute. He spent two years as an economic adviser in Indonesia.

By designating 280 million acres [some 113 million hectares] as permanent forests, Indonesia is protecting and preserving its forests in their natural state. Over 43 per cent of these forests will remain untouched, forever. The other 57 per cent will be carefully managed for sustainable growth.

This statement from the Indonesian Forestry Community appeared in the *Jakarta Post* in January 1994. It is the simple message of a propaganda campaign being conducted worldwide by the commercial interests exploiting Indonesia's tropical forests.

It is an alluring message because it is based on official statistics and it promises good news. Many people in the West are being lulled into acceptance. But the reality of what is happening in the magnificent tropical forests of Indonesia is entirely contrary to the official story. The reality is that extensive areas of tropical forest are being denuded by irresponsible logging, much of it illegal, and many national parks and protected areas are being severely degraded.

As a result, permanent degradation of many forest ecosystems is occurring and many of Indonesia's unique animal and bird species are threatened with imminent extinction. Both claims—that 43 per cent of forests will remain untouched forever and that the other 57 per cent will be carefully managed for sustainable growth—are demonstrably untrue. Perhaps that is why the Indonesian government has recently entered into a $5 million contract with US public relations firm Burson-Marsteller to improve the country's international image on the environment and human rights.

Indonesia's remaining tropical forests are extraordinarily important to the world. In the words of a report by the UN Food and Agriculture Organisation (FAO): 'No other country has the responsibility for more diverse and unique species than does Indonesia'. Indonesia's forests are incredibly rich in species. Although it occupies only 1.3 per cent of the Earth's land surface, within Indonesia can be found 10 per cent of the world's plant species, 12 per cent of the world's mammal species, 16 per cent of the reptile species and 17 per cent of the bird species. Indonesia also has the longest list of species threatened with extinction, even longer than Brazil's.

The government maintains that its forests are managed sustainably under its forest management system, known as the Indonesian Selective Cutting and Replanting system, or TPTI. Few of the hundreds of logging concessions (areas, usually around 100 000 hectares, in which companies are given logging rights) are managed according to the rules, but even within the Ministry of Forestry itself it is acknowledged that application of the TPTI is not sustainable. In addition, most logging companies flagrantly disregard the rules causing widespread and permanent damage.

Some of the worst damage to the tropical forests from logging (which began on a wide scale in Indonesia in the early 1970s) is caused by road-building. Up to 30 per cent of the logged forest area is put under roads, tracks and log landings. Heavy machinery used for extracting logs damages the soils, and log dumps are left covered in machine oil which both clogs the soil and washes into streams. Roads are often carelessly laid out and cut into steep hills causing severe erosion. It is estimated that 13 tonnes of soil are washed off each hectare each month from a new road. It is conservatively estimated that around 39 million cubic metres of soil is eroded from production forests each year, equivalent to an annual mound of soil 1 metre high covering an area of 39 square kilometres.

Erosion is causing the rivers and streams to become silted up. Silt in the water has a scouring effect as it is washed downstream, destroying the habitat of bottom-dwelling creatures. Fish communities decline sharply. Dams and estuaries become silted up, reducing their economic and ecological values.

The logging itself is generally carried out without regard for the damage done to the forest. In extracting a tree of commercial value several other trees are usually killed or damaged. 'Selective logging' usually leaves up to 50 per cent of trees damaged. It is estimated that 25 per cent of each hectare logged over is left permanently deforested. Overall, the best estimate is that 1.2 million hectares is deforested each year in Indonesia, equivalent to an area measuring 120 kilometres by 10 kilometres. Some of this is due to land clearing for agriculture and some is due to reckless logging.

With extensive logging, the opening of the canopy results in the forest floor becoming hotter and the soil drying out. This creates a hostile environment for the microfauna—beetles, spiders, termites and so on. The microfauna are crucial to the nutrient cycle of the tropical forests.

Logging greatly increases the risk of wildfires by drying out the understorey and leaving large volumes of debris on the ground. Large fires, naturally rare in the dark, moist forests of the tropics, can permanently devastate forest ecosystems. The forest fires of East Kalimantan in 1982–83 were without question one of the greatest environmental disasters of modern times. A huge area, 3.6 million hectares, was burnt out and the smoke from the fires forced the authorities to close Singapore's Changi airport, 1500 kilometres to the west.

The impact of logging on biodiversity—what the Earth loses due to the extinction of species—is cause for grave concern. Local ecosystems are permanently destroyed. The logging roads that crisscross the jungle create a patchwork of biological islands that limit the ranges of many creatures. Many species of birds, butterflies and small mammals have evolved in an environment of constant shade. They will not cross sunlit gaps and, confined to the area bounded by logging roads, are squeezed into smaller territories.

It is indisputable then that logging in the 57 per cent of Indonesia's forests allocated to logging is not sustainable ecologically or economically. Some comfort could perhaps be had from the claim that 43 per cent will 'remain untouched, forever'. These 120 million acres (49 million hectares) lie in national parks, wildlife reserves and protection forests. The picture conjured up by the official statistics is of vast areas of natural forest preserved in perpetuity for their environmental values. The reality is very different.

While some large parks are relatively undisturbed, their future is threatened. Many parks and protected areas, in which logging and agriculture are banned, contain forests that have been severely damaged by illegal logging and other forms of human encroachment. Much of the evidence is contained in a forty volume report on forestry in Indonesia by the UN's FAO, a report that has been suppressed by the government. For example, in South Kalimantan 60 per cent of the area in reserves and 35 per cent of the area in protected forests are grossly deforested.

Some reserves, such as the famous Gunung Leseur in Sumatra, are still in good condition but others, such as Way Kambas in Sumatra and Tanjung Puting in Kalimantan, are dominated by scrub and grassland. According to the FAO:

Indeed, some reserves have become so degraded by logging, small-holder intrusion and human-initiated fire that their conservation value has fallen drastically. Examples are Gunung Niut Perkisson in Kalimantan Barat and Kutai in Kalimantan Timur both of which were, until recently, of global significance.

Parks and reserves cannot be considered sacrosanct. There is evidence of instances in which park status has been granted to an area only after the economic resources have been fully exploited, irrespective of the biological values lost. The Forestry Ministry recently converted most of the Pleihari Wildlife Reserve in South Kalimantan into production forest for logging. The reserve had originally been protected as one of the last remaining habitats of the rare Barking Deer. Former Minister for Forestry, Hasjrul Harahap, who was widely seen as an apologist for rapacious logging companies, reacted to criticism by saying that 'since the deer cannot be found any more, should we maintain it as a reserve?'. The Minister went on to say that the area would not be reconverted into a reserve should the Barking Deer reappear, and we can be quite certain that the concession holder will ensure that no deer will be found there again.

Some estimates suggest that up to a third of Indonesia's total annual log volume is cut illegally. The respected newspaper *Kompas* reported, for instance, that illegal logging is rife in the 120 000 hectare Taman Baru forest reserve in Riau, Sumatra. Around 25 000 hectares or 20 per cent of the reserve has been denuded. The companies responsible for the timber thefts are known to the authorities, the activity has been proceeding for three years and involves 300 employees. The head of the provincial forestry office has promised to take action and punish the companies 'if they are found guilty of wood theft'.

Although the government persistently blames local villagers for illegal logging, the scale of it is such that it could only be carried out by well-financed and properly equipped operations with the collusion

of forestry officials, including senior bureaucrats in Jakarta. It is commonly known that the police and military take bribes to ignore thefts.
Huge log rafts are occasionally tied up on the major rivers in Kalimantan and Irian Jaya because illegal loggers have not paid off the
right people. According to the FAO in 1990: ' . . . despite many vio-
lations, frequently documented in the press, no logging company has
ever been prosecuted for illegal felling of trees on a reserve . . . '

According to the *Economist* magazine, when the Forestry Ministry
tried to fine Barito Pacific logging company $5.4 million for cutting
outside of its concession area (itself an extraordinary action), the
bureaucrats were told to get lost. Barito is owned by Prajogo Pangestu,
one of President Soeharto's wealthy friends.

Logging in Indonesia is an integral part of the political system that
runs on rewards for favours granted. Those in the government, including some dedicated officials in the Ministry of Forestry, who want to
see Indonesia's tropical forests managed for sustained timber yields
and preserved for their ecological values are up against powerful companies that are reaping huge profits from logging. In addition to some
of the wealthiest business people in the country, these interests
include the children of President Soeharto among whose diverse
commercial operations are shares in lucrative logging concessions and
timber processing companies.

Timber baron and head of the forest industry association, Bob
Hasan is often referred to as the real minister for forestry. Any major
decision concerning forests is always approved first by Hasan. Hasan
has launched vigorous attacks on foreign environmentalists accusing
them of ignorance about Indonesia's forests and of being the stooges
of logging interests in the West.

Despite this gloomy picture there are signs that the situation could
change. There are senior officials who recognise that the current situation of gross overexploitation is contrary to the long-run interests
of Indonesia. The new Minister for Forestry, Djamaludin Suryohadi-

kusumo, is said to be much more independent of commercial interests than his predecessor. He appears to be aware of the extent of the problems and is considering some serious measures to try to establish the rule of law in the forests.

There are several environmental organisations in Indonesia that put up a brave fight against enormously powerful interests, exposing much malpractice and destruction. Newspapers are increasingly forthright in reporting illegalities and injustices against local people. The government is especially sensitive to international criticism of its logging industry and has felt compelled to take measures to patch up its international image. Cosmetic measures will be unmasked in the longer term and the government may well be forced to take some substantive measures to retain its place in the world community. While huge amounts of damage are already irreversible, only a few years remain before the great bulk of Indonesia's extraordinary tropical forests are damaged forever.

HOW TO GET A MILLION
TO ONE AND LOSE

———————————

ERIC MAGNUSSON

**ERIC MAGNUSSON teaches in the School of
Chemistry at ADFA and, consequently, is interested
in the presentation of science in the classroom and
in the courtroom.**

Since its invention in the mid 1980s, the forensic use of DNA profiling
has never been far from the headlines. Taking DNA test results to court
has become rather like gift-wrapping a toy giraffe. You struggle to get
the head tied up and then a foot sticks out. You just get the back legs
under control and meanwhile the front legs come loose.

I predict it will stay that way for quite a while yet. One thing that
will keep it in the hard-to-wrap category is the tendency for people
to concentrate on the big numbers. 'The odds against these two DNA
profiles coming from different persons are a *million to one.*' Or even
a *billion.* Now, just consider the psychology of these numbers for a
minute.

A major problem with these big numbers is that they seem to
remove the necessity to consider any other possibility. A prosecutor
can say, as one did recently: 'Well, suppose we did overestimate the
odds. Suppose it isn't a hundred million, suppose only one million to

one. Suppose only a hundred thousand!! . . . still damning.' He sounds very generous but he's not. Not if one of the other possibilities is that the DNA shouldn't even be in the evidence.

To make the point clear, consider a scenario. A crime has occurred in a major city. A woman and her partner have been murdered. There's only one suspect. Sounds familiar? Anyway, he's interviewed. He agrees for a police nurse to take a blood sample for DNA testing and tells the detectives that there's blood in his car and at home because he cut himself a day or two ago. His profile is matched with several blood samples from the crime scene and several incriminating matches of his DNA profile are found. There was a lot of blood around. I apologise for setting up the story this way—all this blood—but it was a knife murder and so . . .

My purpose is to make a point about the need to be very careful with big numbers. Suppose the evidence comes to court like this. The prosecution report very careful DNA testing of samples from blood obtained at the murder scene and from the reference samples taken from the suspect and from the two victims. The latter, obviously, are in excellent condition because there're plenty of samples and because the samples are chemically preserved, but some of the samples on the ground, under the hot sun, are degraded and not all give useable profiles.

There's blood on the gate at the back of the victim's house and it is likely that the killer used the gate when he ran away. The police don't notice it when they go over the crime scene on the first day but it is there three days later and they're able to sample a fair amount. The bloodstain contains fairly large amounts of DNA and it proves to match bands from the sample given to the police by the suspect. This is pretty damaging evidence by itself, but there's a lot more than this.

During the investigation the police searched the suspect's house and took large quantities of clothing which were carefully checked at the crime lab. One item brought to court and shown to the jury is a sock with obvious dried blood on it. The DNA result from it is also highly incriminating—bands matching those of the female victim. Because the DNA is in good condition, tests from multiple positions in the genome are reported giving odds like 'million to one against the chance occurrence of such a match with the victim's profile'. There's also a pair of gloves, one of which was found at the suspect's home. The other was found at the crime scene. It is soaked in blood. The jury are shown it and are directed to look away from the dried blood to a small smear near the button of the wrist. It's almost too little to treat but the forensic laboratory is pretty diligent and they finally get enough DNA for a profile and the bands match the suspect. Suspect's blood on a glove found at the murder site and soaked with the victims' blood! So the incriminating DNA evidence mounts up.

Then there's DNA from the drops of blood on the ground, recovered by crime scene officers using a cloth dampened with distilled water. Each cloth is placed in a clean plastic bag and, as with all the other evidence, entered into the record under the number allocated to the case. These samples turn out to be hard to process. It's hard to pick up much blood from the ground and, anyway, it gets pretty degraded in the sun in the interval between crime and collection. But some can be profiled and, surprisingly, the profiles show the suspect's bands. Not very strong, but unmistakable. Again, very unlikely that they matched just by chance. Odds of millions to one against the possibility that they got there from some other person.

Well, let's wrap this up quickly. We'll have the prosecution also telling the court about blood from one other source. Police impounded a vehicle belonging to the suspect. There's blood on the seat and console, not much, only smears apparently, and it's not in good condition, but there's enough for testing by the extremely sensitive PCR method now used routinely in Australia and around the world. However, the quality of the result isn't too high. Apparently the DNA is pretty badly degraded. Later in the investigation they examine the vehicle again and find traces of blood not seen before. And the results are much clearer. DNA from both the early and the late samples matches the suspect's profile and there's no surprise in that—given his remark during the interview about cutting himself in the vehicle. On a mobile phone bracket. But what does incriminate him is the fact that the samples, both of them, produce too many bands for one person. And the extra bands match DNA from the *victims*. And again, naturally, there are the big numbers. Big odds against coincidental matches.

Right, so there's the prosecution case. It's rare for DNA evidence to be all there is in a criminal trial but in this scenario we'll make it the major part of the case against the suspect. So, we'll have the prosecution explain the science of DNA profiling ... very carefully ... how the nucleic acid is extracted—in quantities measured in billionths of a gram (nanograms), how the DNA segments inherited at one particular location in one chromosome are singled out from all the hundreds of thousands of other segments, and finally show up as the 'bands' you see on the autorad. Finally, how the forensic scientists compare the profiles from victim and suspect in the case with many different profiles collected from people in the community. As measured in crime laboratories, a DNA profile won't be unique, but each person's profile will be very rare. So the scientists use the profiles from the community to measure how rare it is. Then they can calculate the likelihood that DNA from some other person could produce bands in the same positions. This is where the big numbers come from. Even when genes at only a few locations are probed, a person's DNA profile is so close to individual that the odds against some other person producing the same one, one that matches, can be large. A million to one, a hundred million to one, a billion to one.

So, as usual, the prosecution goes through all that. They explain the science and describe the technology. They display the autorads prepared from the blood spatters on the footpath, the bloodstains on the gate, the smears on gloves and sock and seat and console in the vehicle. They point out the damning similarities between bands from the crime scene and bands from the blood sample collected by the nurse from the suspect. They hand the autorads into the jury box so they can see for themselves the obvious similarities between the victims' bands and the bands from the samples that they got from the belongings seized from the accused.

Okay, prosecution case finished, defence case begins. It's pretty boring if the jury just finds him guilty. What defence can we suggest for a trial on *Ockham's Razor*? Does the accused have any chance at all? Against odds of a million to one?

Well, this accused is going to be pretty vigorously defended. Not by disputing the DNA, not by trying to confuse the jury with long-winded explanations of the statistics. The defence is suspicious about the overall appearance of the results and so, before the trial, they get independent experts to go over things. Legal Aid won't always come to the party for that but, for *Ockham's Razor*, we'll assume they've got enough money and they get independent experts to check things out.

They find that the blood on the gate (remember, from the sample that wasn't seen at first), gave good quality DNA in good quantity. So there was a good clear result. Unlike the blood on the footpath, not very far away, that only yielded a result after enormous effort. DNA degrades quickly on a hot footpath . . . why was it preserved so well only half a metre away on the metal gate? So they say to themselves, 'planted there'. If planted there, planted from where? Most likely from the reference sample given by the accused. And if from the reference sample, it would contain chemical preservative. That would explain why it was so good when stains nearby were degraded. So, check for preservative! Oh, yes, and it wasn't seen at first, was it? And after three days it turned up.

Now, of course, a defence like that needs to be notified. Prosecution is told and sends the sample away to another forensic laboratory to check for EDTA, the preservative. Report comes back, no EDTA. Prosecution is relieved. But defence demands the scientific results and gives them to its own expert. He reports EDTA.

And this comes out in court. Defence expert says, 'EDTA clearly present. Amount small, but consistent with the amount remaining from a chemically preserved blood sample.' Prosecution expert says, 'too little'. Defence expert says, 'not too little'. Defence lawyer says to prosecution expert, 'Have you ever tested to see how much EDTA would remain in a blood sample kept like this?' 'No' says the expert.

Defence turns to the sock and the sock evidence turns out to be suspicious too. Amazingly, the first person to investigate it and check it for blood reports that no blood is obvious. Later, another investigator finds a large bloodstain. The socks are dark in colour but when held up to the jury, the bloodstain can be seen across the court. And the blood is well preserved. It's no surprise that the defence ask if there might be EDTA in this one too. The answer is the same as before. The *Ockham's Razor* jury look at each other. Then the defence mentions the second bloodspot on the sock. On the inside surface opposite the first stain, says the lawyer. No objection from the prosecution. You can imagine the first stain getting on the sock from, say, a victim, covered in blood, falling to the floor ... a finger covered in blood touches the murderer's sock. But now. Obviously there was no person in the sock when the blood, wet blood, was transferred from the first position to the second. And, they say, 'we've measured how long it takes for a person to get from the murder site to the house where they found the sock. It's longer than the time it takes for blood to coagulate.' Prosecution can say nothing.

The defence, now no longer content with raising doubt about the integrity of the sample, start to check out the record-keeping of the forensic laboratory. They discover that some blood is missing. So they question the lab assistant who transferred the blood samples to tubes for testing. He finally remembers that he spilled some. That's the explanation for the missing blood. It spilled. 'Where did you spill it?' 'In the evidence processing room.' 'What happened?' 'It spurted up through the Chemwipe and it got on my gloves.' So, a man who is preparing samples from the crime scene for testing spills a fresh sample of the very blood that people are going to look for in those samples. Using a method that's so sensitive it's capable of detecting nanograms of DNA, the amount you get in a speck of blood—almost too small to see.

I hardly need to go on, the point's been made. You can have fantastically high odds but if the samples are contaminated or if you're getting false positives when you do the tests or if the bloodstain was planted, the samples mean nothing. It's no good making a few concessions, saying 'Okay, it's not a million to one, it's only half a million'. If the evidence was planted, the odds collapse. A million doesn't go to half a million, it goes to zero.

Of course, as crime-watchers knew all along, the scenario I gave you was not imaginary. That evidence about blood on the gate and blood on the sock really was presented to a jury. The words 'Where is it, Mr Fung?' were actually said last year in a well-publicised court case in the United States. The sample from the gate got a lot of attention. After watching it on television a lot of Americans now know a lot about DNA profiles.

The information about the way the evidence samples were handled was *not* so well publicised. I became aware of it after a discussion with Bill Thompson, a lawyer who teaches in the University of California and does research on the use of forensic science evidence in criminal courts in the United States. He was one of the first to notice that DNA evidence was not always presented fairly in US courts and quickly got a reputation for being a lawyer able to analyse the evidence. This led to his being approached to become a member of the O.J. Simpson defence team. Clearly, therefore, he's not a disinterested observer of the case. However, I tried to make my scenario correspond to the evidence as it was presented during the trial.

So, should the jury have heard the DNA evidence? If you'd been accused and your blood had been handled like that, would you be happy for the jury to hear lawyers talking about matching profiles and big odds? A better way would be for courts to decide if the evidence is safe at the pre-trial stage. They usually only decide that in the appeal court after the jury has been exposed to the evidence and perhaps prejudiced by it . . . after the verdict. But courts have rules for 'verbals' and for alibis and so on. Maybe we need some rules for science and for collecting scientific evidence.

This is the twentieth century and we need to use twentieth century tools to make sure that the jury is hearing evidence that's safe for them to hear. Big numbers are safe when every link in the chain that holds is strong. But using the strength of the final link to suggest that every other link is also strong is not a good twentieth century idea.

CRISIS? WHAT CRISIS?

CLIVE McFARLAND

CLIVE McFARLAND is a Senior Research Scientist with the Biomaterials group at CSIRO's Division of Bio-molecular Engineering, and a project leader with the Cooperative Research Centre for Cardiac Technology.

If, like me, you collect interesting facial expressions, try this the next time you're at a party. Turn to the person next to you and casually ask, 'So what do you make of the biomaterials situation?' Odds are you'll be rewarded with a fine example of 'stunned mullet' expression number 34—you know, the one your son gives you when you ask him to tidy his room. But ask for opinions on breast implants and you'll get a much livelier reaction.

The current legal, social and scientific controversy over these implants has dramatically increased public awareness about the implantation of materials and devices into the body. And while the scientific jury is still out on the question of breast implants, scrutiny of medical devices and the biomaterials from which they're made is at an all-time high. And rightly so. It's when scrutiny becomes scare-mongering that we have to ask if we are best serving the needs of that 6 or so per cent of us who will receive an implant at some stage in our lives. After all, for many of us biomaterials are part of our lives (and indeed, part of our bodies).

The plastic in your contact lens is a biomaterial. So's the electrode in Uncle John's pacemaker, or the stainless steel in Granny's hip joint. Interestingly, of the range of materials approved for clinical use, only a couple were developed as biomaterials; the rest have been adapted from other applications. And we've been doing it for a long time. Survival for early man was difficult at the best of times, and our ancestors soon realised that the materials used to stitch hides together could just as well be used to repair Og the Hunter after a close encounter with the business end of some of the local wildlife. Some would argue that this stitching-up process marked the start of the legal profession, but that's another story.

As our skills in working materials grew, so did our ability to use them in medical applications. Goldsmiths in ancient Greece used their precious metal to repair the skull surrounding the precious human brain. A few hundred years later, the Romans were replacing limbs with external prostheses. The flowering of knowledge that marked the Renaissance laid the foundations for many new processes, such as the glassblowing techniques which would form the basis for the manufacture of glass contact lenses some two hundred years later. And in the 1800s bone defects were being repaired with ivory, held in place by collagen glues. These glues failed in the hostile environment of the body, but the arrival of the industrial revolution sparked the development of a whole range of materials crucial to the production of biomaterials.

The development of the chemical industry resulted in the availability of new synthetic materials. In the 1940s, synthetic polymers were used in biomaterial applications. There's a well-known story about a Second World War fighter pilot who was shot down, patched up and sent back into the fray. Only some time later was it discovered that minute fragments from the Perspex windscreen of his aircraft had become lodged in his eye. The lack of adverse reaction to this material led to its adoption as a ophthalmic biomaterial. Whether this story is true or not, it demonstrates nicely how biomaterials research freely borrows from other disciplines.

And we need this broad base of expertise. Let's consider for a minute just what is needed if you're going to replace part of the body with a substitute component. Firstly, there's the engineering side of things. Traditionally this is how biomaterials have been developed. You need to replace a bone? Fine. You'll need something strong and fairly rigid, but not brittle. Metal would seem to be a good choice here, but the body is a very corrosive environment so that rules out many metals, and so on. What sorts of loads and stresses will it be subjected to? The design of the human body has left us with some engineering nightmares.

Imagine you have developed the world's most sophisticated computer. It weighs a few pounds, and you need it to move from place to place. You ask an engineer to design a self-propelling cradle for your fragile, sophisticated machine, and they suggest perching it on the top of a 2 metre high free-standing column with two sets of hinges in it, and which moves by continuously toppling forwards. You'd sack your engineer on the spot, but this is exactly the situation evolution has created for the human brain.

Now think about what one of those sets of hinges, the knee joint, has to endure. It has to support the weight of the body, survive the impact each time a foot hits the ground, permit any number of rugged activities, and do it all hundreds of times per day. These considerations alone mean that the design of an artificial knee joint is no trivial matter.

Say we go with a metal for strength: the metal-to-metal contact in the hinge region won't give us that smooth articulating surface we need. So let's give it a slippery coating, maybe the teflon used in non-stick frying pans. But how thick does this coating need to be? How will we bond it to the metal? And so on.

But let's just assume that all the engineering problems are solved, the graph paper put away, and the mechanical testers turned off. We now have to consider the environment we're placing our newly designed joint into: the human body. And here we come up against a living, breathing, wilful, exasperating, unpredictable, wonderful organism: in short, we come up against biology.

Earlier I referred to the hostile environment of the body: this was a mistake, surely? After all, is this not the very body that we suckle and nurture, which supports and sustains us, which grows and heals itself, in which we live, laugh, sleep, make love? Hostile? How can it be hostile? Well if you're an invading bacterium, a virus, or even a lovingly designed titanium knee joint, the human body is the last place you want to be, believe me. Millennia of evolutionary refinement have armed the body with an arsenal that Bruce Willis would die for (and probably has). And this massive offensive capacity is unleashed against any foreign invader, be it a bacterium bent on mass slaughter, or an implant designed to save life.

Assuming we've chosen our materials carefully so at least they're not toxic and they don't cause the host to mount an immediate counterattack, what of the longer term effects? How do we engineer an appropriate response from the body? For example, if we're making a vascular graft, ideally we'd like it to promote the adhesion of the endothelial cells which normally line our blood vessels, thereby mimicking what nature does. Well, we can make it sticky to get cells to attach, but what's to stop other things like platelets sticking? A pile of platelets stuck on a surface can form the solid plug known in the trade as a thrombus, and that's the last thing you'd want in your newly repaired blood vessel.

If all this sounds frightening, consider what we're attempting to do here; replace millennia of evolution with a few years of mankind's technological tinkering. To me, the amazing thing is not that some implants fail, it's that the vast majority work as well as they do. Now I know you can argue that hip joints only succeed because their elderly recipients wear out before they do, but try telling that to a pensioner who's just received a reprieve from a lifetime's pain. I'd suggest that the ideal biomaterial is one which immediately restores lost function, and is subsequently replaced by the body with a new functional tissue: 'tissue engineering' as it's become known. And this is a big ask.

Take an apparently simple tissue like cartilage: the lump of gristle which provides the slippery surface that our joints need to work properly. Often thought of fairly disparagingly: no blood supply, not many nerves, a woven fibrous matrix containing a jelly-like substance, and a few cells called chondrocytes which aren't exactly overactive. 'Chondrocytes are so stupid they don't even know when they're dead,' I was once told. But can we make a synthetic self-repairing cartilage? No. But we're making steps towards it.

With the realisation of the complexity of the job we expect biomaterials to do comes the need for greater understanding of the mechanisms involved. And that, of course, means research. And research that has the advantage of being both fundamentally important and having practical applications. Fundamental importance? Well, here's an example.

Our bodies are composed of tissues, and those tissues are made up of cells in a specialised environment, usually some sort of matrix which they make, repair and restructure as required. Traditionally regarded as a rather boring scaffold which supports the infinitely more exciting cells, we now know that this matrix does far more; it allows cells to talk to each other, it stores chemical messengers, it transmits environmental signals, and much more. Logic tells us that the cells must have anchors to fasten themselves to this matrix, and indeed they do in the form of receptors built into the cell wall. These receptors bind to this scaffold, and as well as anchoring the cells enable communication into and out of the matrix. So far so good.

So what happens when we implant a material in the body? Very often it becomes colonised by cells which attach to it and start performing their cellular duties: this can be a good or bad thing, depending on the situation. But the question I want to address is this: why should cells stick at all? With the best will in the world, it's hard to envisage that cells would have evolved receptors to materials like stainless steel or titanium, so how do they stick to them? Well, it turns out that within milliseconds of placing a foreign material in the body, proteins are adsorbed from the body fluids onto its surface. Cells which have the appropriate receptors stick down via this layer of adsorbed protein. Change the protein layer, and you change the cell response.

Now this is fundamental, exciting stuff. It's the stuff of how cells work, of how tumour cells spread: it's the very stuff of life itself. And it's pretty useful in biomaterials research, too. Remember our vascular graft problem? Well, researchers in the United States found a receptor on endothelial cells which wasn't present on platelets. So they built the bit of the protein which that receptor bound to, and glued it onto the surface of their graft. Result? Endothelial cells recognise the bit of protein and stick to it via their receptors. Platelets, bereft of this receptor, float away in search of a more promising home. Neat, eh?

But as exciting as this work is, we still can't make our self-repairing implant. And curiously enough, one of the problems is that we don't know enough about what makes a successful biomaterial. We know a fair bit about why they fail: a whole raft of specialists diagnose, remove, examine and repair failed implants, but the successful ones pass away quietly with their hosts, taking the secrets of their success with them to the grave. We need to uncover these secrets: we need to give good implants the same attention as their less well-behaved brethren. And to do this we need to know the implant's life story, from its design and manufacture through implantation and clinical history, and finally to death, hopefully at a ripe old age and through natural causes.

And if implant design is an engineering nightmare, then implant tracking is a logistical one. But this need is recognised by the research

97

community, and a worldwide series of tracking workshops is being held: the last one was in Melbourne, under the auspices of the Australian Society for Biomaterials. Apart from obvious questions like who will pay for the tracking process, a number of fascinating aspects have come to light, such as who owns the implant anyway? And while we're pondering broader ethical, philosophical and sociological questions, what about implant psychology? No, I don't mean counselling for over-stressed knee joints, or motivating weary pacemakers. I'm talking about how we can help those of us who receive implants.

Think about this. An implanted cardiac defibrillator does what it says: it monitors heart performance and corrects any irregularities with an electrical impulse. Modern defibs do this in a fairly sophisticated fashion, but there is nevertheless the possibility that without warning 500 volts will be dropped across the heart. Imagine living with the possibility that at any time your heart rate alters dramatically you may be kicked in the chest by a powerful and invisible racehorse, and you start to get the idea. Now I can think of at least one very pleasurable activity in which a racing heart is an integral part, but in this case the question 'Did the earth move for you?' can take on a new and sinister meaning. In fact, this is a very rare occurrence, and to answer the other frequently asked question in this situation, no your partner would not receive a similar shock. But you do begin to see the need for education and counselling.

In this brief look at biomaterials we've considered the roles of a whole range of expertise from materials scientists and engineers, through cell biologists and chemists, clinicians and pathologists, to philosophers and counsellors. And inevitably we have to add the legal profession to this list, so let's return to the issue of breast implants. In the United States, several women who had experienced problems after they received silicon breast implants sued the supplier. This small company promptly went bankrupt, and because of the way the law works in the States, the chain of litigation passed along from supplier to supplier, eventually ending at Dow Corning, a subsidiary of the industrial giant Dow Chemical Company, who have statutory approval to manufacture medical-grade silicone. The weight of claims totalling $7 billion may well mean that Dow Corning will file for bankruptcy, but in the meantime they have withdrawn their other medical materials from the market. Hard to blame them: there's little money in biomaterials, since they make up less than 2 per cent of the value of an implant. Most of the profit comes when the materials are fabricated into medical devices. In any case, medical polymers form only a tiny fraction of Dow's market. Why risk being litigated to insolvency over something which doesn't bring in much revenue in the first place?

Many other manufacturers, seeing the writing on the wall, have followed suit. The critical point is that to the best of our knowledge, these other embargoed materials have been good performers, and have significantly enhanced the quality of life of the vast majority of people who have received them. And that's a lot of people: over 11 million in the United States alone.

This takes us straight to the heart of a classic debate: the rights of the individual balanced against the needs of society. Should I, in legitimately pursuing my claim over my silicone implant, deprive you of your hip replacement? Or your heart valve? Or whatever? I believe the answer is clearly no. But what can be done about it? Well, the US House of Representatives and Senate currently have before them product liability bills: the so-called 'Common Sense' legislation, which limits the liability of raw materials manufacturers, and that's a start. But in the meantime we're relying on stockpiles of many of these materials. And after that? This can be regarded either as a global crisis or as an opportunity, allowing new players to enter the field, probably as small companies supplying niche markets. But whatever way you look at it, what we all need as researchers, as manufacturers, as legislators but most, most of all as recipients of biomaterials, is a good strong dose of common sense.

A MAN AND
HIS DOG

BILL WILLIAMS

Dr BILL WILLIAMS, a regular contributor to Ockham's Razor, was known to many people as 'the barefoot botanist'. He died in October 1995.

I want to talk about the relationship between dogs and men. Anybody writing a script on this subject immediately encounters a linguistic problem. When I was a small boy struggling with Latin I was caused to learn a small rhyme beginning 'Common are to either sex/Artifex and Opifex'. These are what are called in the trade *epicene* nouns; they are gender-neutral, carrying no implication of male or female. English is oddly short of epicene nouns and pronouns; and I refuse to use sentences beginning 'man or woman and his or her dog or bitch'; I shall firmly talk about 'man and his dog', leaving the other half to be understood; and if the feral feminists don't like it, it's just too bad.

Books on dogs come in two types. Books of type one, the overwhelming majority, are essentially anecdotal, written about specific dogs by people who have known and loved them: books like Jilly Cooper's delightful *Intelligent and Loyal*, the numerous articles by James Thurber, later collected into the anthology *Thurber's Dogs*, and of course the two volumes of working-dog stories, collected and published by the ABC. Type two is much rarer; it critically examines the man/dog relationship, and I possess only two examples. Campbell's *Behaviour Problems in Dogs* is important and impressive, though perhaps a trifle over-serious; he contrives to give the impression that the world is full of problem dogs, and even fuller of problem owners. I haven't found this; I know almost all the dogs in my immediate neighbourhood, and regard them all as essentially 'doggy-mates'. The other book is Desmond Morris's *Dogwatching*. I should confess that I have a great respect for Desmond Morris. Many years ago—when he was, I think, Curator of Mammals at the London Zoo—he and I often sat together on the BBC science-quiz program *Who Knows?*. I much enjoyed his *The Naked Ape*, *The Human Zoo* and *The Book of Ages*.

In *Dogwatching* he argues that the dog has been bred from the wolf, not, as once believed, from the jackal; and he sets out a number of pertinent parallels between the social organisation of wolf packs and man packs. Yet, much as I admire the book, I sometimes wonder whether he has ever actually agreed to share his life with a dog, because despite my respect for his knowledge there are two points on which I think he is wrong, and one point I think he has missed.

The first point is simple: I can't accept his views on the underlying doggy psychology of tail-wagging; but we can let that pass. The second point is more important: he seems to believe that a dog naturally accepts his owner as the leader of his pack. I suppose this might be true if one started with a very young puppy, which I never have, but in my experience if you take a more or less mature dog into your home, said dog is apt to decide that he is going to be Boss Dog, and you are going to be Inferior Dog—number two in the pack. Moreover, a dog can be remarkably efficient in reorganising the household arrangements to suit itself. My present dog is a two-year-old Border-Collie-cross bitch called Shannon. She is an early-morning dog. Shortly before first light—in Townsville that's between about 4.30 and

5.30 am—she clambers on my bed and licks me awake. When she is satisfied that I have recovered consciousness, she returns to her beloved yard. However, if I haven't surfaced within about ten minutes, she reappears, takes a running leap and lands on my middle with a resounding thump, making it clear that it is time for her walk. So, sleepily but obediently, I put on a pair of shorts and we set off. This may sound easy, but you'd be surprised. I don't know whether people still read the work of the Canadian philosopher and humourist Stephen Leacock, but anybody who does will remember his vivid account of the knight who, at the moment of crisis, 'leapt on his horse and galloped off in all directions'.

This is a precise description of Shannon's concept of a walk. So I am, as you might say, yanked hither and yon to the amusement of anybody we happen to pass, who often resort to the traditional chiacking 'Hey—who's taking who for a walk?'. Everybody says she should go to obedience classes, but that is easier said than done. The only obedience class I know is held on the other side of town—I haven't a car, and it has recently become illegal to take dogs in taxis. So I am resigned to remaining a pupil, obedience-trained by Shannon. She must regard me as an apt pupil, since at the slightest suggestion she is always willing to take me out for a walk.

Obedience training has become not merely an industry but almost a cult, of which, some years ago, the high priestess was undoubtedly Barbara Woodhouse. In his *The Book of Ages*, Desmond Morris calls her 'English dog-trainer extraordinary', whose teaching sessions on television intimidated dog owners even more than their pets. Some of her oracular statements will long be remembered, such as 'The Japanese don't seem to know much about obedience', by which of course she meant canine obedience training. But her most famous edict, which convulsed an irreverent studio audience, and which surely deserves an entry in any future Dictionary of Quotations, was 'To reward a male, scratch him between the legs'.

More seriously, the human/dog relation is seen at its most valuable when the human is aged, sick or disabled. We all know the superb work done by Guide Dogs for the Blind. Less well known is the fact that they are sometimes able to provide a dog for what has become known as 'pet therapy'. It has long been known that people who keep a pet live longer than those who don't; and increasingly it has been found that the introduction of a friendly dog to a nursing home, old people's home, or whatever, does wonders for the morale and happiness of the inmates. I can vouch for this from personal experience. A few years ago I lay for weeks unconscious in Intensive Care, and was not expected to recover. A friendly sister at the hospital—perhaps feeling that, whatever the regulations, anything might be worth trying— allowed a friend to bring my then dog (Joe, the predecessor of Shannon) to see me; and so, for a little while, he lay beside me. I am told that, unconscious though I was, I automatically put out my hand to caress him, and was rewarded by a few comforting licks. To the surprise of the doctors, I *did* recover; and I believe that the keen sense of love and loyalty that was able to penetrate even the mists of unconsciousness in which I was embedded contributed to my recovery.

Perhaps the most familiar literary image is that of the old man and his dog, dozing peacefully beside the fire. Do you remember John Masefield's poem 'On Growing Old'? It begins, 'Be with me Beauty, for the fire is dying,/My dog and I are old, too old for roving.' But there is an important point here, the point that I think Desmond Morris has missed. Why should a lonely old man choose a dog for a companion, instead of another human being? The key to this riddle can be found in Shakespeare, in *Coriolanus*; for it was Coriolanus who addressed his wife as 'my gracious silence'. The power of articulate speech has given man access to all the knowledge of the world, and has ensured his pre-eminent position in the animal kingdom. But there is a downside: because he can talk, man too often can't stop talking. A human being, sooner or later, will feel obliged to say something, and his companion will feel obliged to reply; there could even arise an argument. But a dog offers silent companionship; and in this gracious silence there need be no more than a gentle scratch behind the ear, acknowledged by an affectionate lick. No more is asked, and no more is needed.

But are dogs intelligent enough to be companions? Of course they are. I'm not thinking of their ability to be trained for incredibly complex tasks, such as we see in sheepdog trials, and years ago used to see in performing dogs on stage. In one episode of the ABC science show series *The Pinnacle of Life* it was argued that the test of true intelligence is the ability to think ahead, usually exemplified by the monkey who piled up boxes to enable him to reach a coveted banana. Well, dogs can do this too. In the program Miriam Rothschild provided a delightful story of her two dogs: a lovable but slightly dumb Labrador and a very alert young Collie, both of whom coveted the same armchair, which the Labrador usually got first. The Collie worked out a strategy to deal with this: he went into the yard, retrieved a favourite tennis ball, and dropped it in the lounge. The Labrador, who could never resist a ball, lumbered after it; by the time he had got it the Collie was firmly esconced in the armchair. There was an even more hilarious example on the London stage in the '30s. The London Coliseum had—still has, for all I know—a large revolving stage; and one impressario thought up the idea of presenting, as a variety turn, terriers chasing an electric rat. The rat was fixed; the terriers were racing hell-for-leather on the stage, which was turning in the opposite direction, so that the progress of the race remained in view of the audience. However, it took only a minute or two for first one dog, then others, to realise that this whole procedure was just plain silly. They worked out that if you ran in the other direction, or even just sat down, the rat would, as it were, come to you. This of course brought the house down and stopped the show. I don't think there was a second performance.

But joys too often have their attendant sorrows. The minor sorrow arises every day: that look of disappointment and reproach when it becomes clear that you are going out, and on this occasion can't take your dog with you. The major sorrow arises because man, with his longer lifespan, often outlives his dog. There comes the dreadful day when the vet shakes his head, and says he is sorry, but there is nothing more he can do. And so, fighting back the tears, you bow to the inevitable, give a last caress and murmur of farewell, as, desolate, you watch an important part of your life being gently led away.

I suppose it might help if you were religious, for then the possibility of reunion would not be quite inconceivable. I was thinking of Cicely Hamilton's charming little story *A Kitten in Paradise*. In this, a disreputable old tramp who once, faced with a starving kitten, in a moment of drunken generosity pinched somebody's bottle of milk and poured it out for the kitten, so ensuring the kitten's literally undying love. Years later, the tramp appears at the gate of heaven so besmirched with sin that there is no hope that he will be allowed in. Suddenly, there is a tiny cry of welcome from behind the gate; it is the kitten he had befriended. The angel guarding the gate said: 'You may enter, for until you came, one of the blessed could not know the fullness of joy. The Lord has need of you, to make glad the heart of His kitten.'

But for those of us without a religion, the loss is irrevocable, the desolation complete. Kipling understood this very well when, in his poem 'The Power of the Dog' he wrote, 'Brothers and Sisters, I bid you beware/Of giving your heart to a dog to tear'.

We go on doing it. Might it be that, after the cataclysm at the end of the Cretaceous, the arising mammals needed the help and companionship of each other, regardless of species? If so, most of the ability of mammal to call to mammal has now gone; but one interspecific bond remains. I believe that, so long as the Earth endures, so will endure the companionship between a man and his dog.

EPILEPSY SURGERY—SOME
PERSONAL OBSERVATIONS

SUZANNE YANKO

**SUZANNE YANKO is a Melbourne-based education
journalist and writer whose book *Coming to Terms
With Epilepsy* was published in 1993.**

It was certainly news to me when, nearly three years ago, my neurologist told me that surgery could possibly put an end to the epileptic seizures I suffered, since they were the type known as 'complex-partial', apparently emanating from the right temporal lobe of the brain.

The diagnostic techniques used are 'space-age', as I discovered when I went through the testing process in late 1990 and in the following year had a successful temporal lobectomy. I had not been looking for a dramatic 'one-off' solution to the problem of the complex-partial seizures I suffered. After all, I'd put up with these disorienting episodes for ten years before a diagnosis of epilepsy was made, and the relatively low dosage of my medication now had things reasonably under control with few side-effects—apart from an embarrassing tendency to go to sleep across the dinner table! So . . . why consider surgery?

It was the results of a magnetic-resonance imaging test which offered this possibility. This test, which involves detecting minute changes in the brain when it is subjected to a strong magnetic field, involved lying still for about an hour with my head in a white Ned Kelly-type helmet.

It was similar to a CAT scan, although it took longer for the machine to take its pictures, making a subdued drumming noise while it did so. The MRI results clearly showed that the two temporal lobes of my brain were different from each other, the right having a sort of smudge on it, making it look bigger than the left. That 'smudge' on the MRI indicated scar tissue, and tallied with an EEG showing some intermittent unusual activity on the right side of the brain.

Although I had been dutifully taking medication for eight months, the MRI was the first tangible evidence—as far as I was concerned—that the doctors were indeed right. I was more overwhelmed by the relief that I had not been imagining those moments of disorientation which the doctors called 'complex-partial seizures'; I was not slowly going crazy!

It was ironic that just as I'd accepted that I had epilepsy, the neurologist was offering the possibility of a temporal lobectomy—removal of the part of the temporal lobe which had been identified as the source of the epilepsy. There were many 'ifs', as the doctor stressed:

- surgery was suitable only in a minority of cases; whether I was among them could be established only by intensive tests as a hospital in-patient.
- temporal lobectomy was intended to significantly reduce epileptic seizures, not to save a life. Those operations which were performed had a success rate of about 80 per cent but it was important to note the 2 per cent risk of stroke or other danger associated with any operation. In most of the remaining cases there was a diminishing of seizures, which might be more gradual, and there could be some impairment of memory or other functions.
- there was no urgency, I could take as long as I liked to decide and could withdraw from the program at any point if I changed my mind.

I decided to go ahead . . . at least with the testing program. It was easier to agree to enter hospital for tests than to commit oneself to having surgery. And the tests might well prove that surgery was not a option after all.

So, after a wait of nearly two months—and with only a day's notice—I was admitted to the Austin hospital for what I expected to be a prolonged stay in the monitoring room. I'd packed in a hurry, and soon realised my sweater-type tops would not do. Because in the monitoring room you are attached day and night to an EEG machine, so only tops which open at the front with full-length zips or buttons will do.

There were distractions to relieve the tedium of the monitoring room; a large television set accompanies the video camera which is trained on you twenty-four hours a day; the bonus is you can watch the TV as the camera watches you! I had a good supply of the cryptic crosswords I usually do; if I couldn't get much physical exercise, at least I could feel my brain was still working!

The process began in earnest when the EEG technologists arrived to put me 'on the wires'. About twenty wires run from the EEG machine to a small pouch containing a sort of junction-box; this has a cable which marries the EEG information to the videotape and also connects with the 'patient's wires' which—as with any EEG—end in the little discs which are glued to the patient's head. It doesn't hurt— at least, no more than having pins put in at the hairdresser's. The result looks less than glamorous, however, expecially as lengths of crepe bandage are then wound round and round the head to keep the wires in place. A sister from the neurology ward commented that a patient's five-year-old son was concerned that 'Daddy must have a very sore head' when he saw the extensive bandaging, and even nursing staff new to the ward have wondered at first what injuries might be concealed by such huge 'turbans'!

Central to the room is a large chair which is 'home' for the patient, day and night. Mobility in the monitoring room is extremely restricted. The wires are just long enough for you to reach a small washbasin in the room and to use a bedpan which is placed on a chair behind the door—thankfully, out of camera range. But, you are like a horse in a small stall until your seizures have been picked up and recorded to the point where the doctors have the clear and unambiguous information they need. The equipment in the monitoring room is there for round-the-clock observation; the video camera will record the way you look and behave during a seizure and the EEG can pick up any unusual electrical activity in the brain.

This is not as impersonal as it seems. It allows, as one doctor put it to me, 'good old-fashioned clinical observation with twentieth century technology'. No one who has experienced the monitoring room would describe it as being similar to staying in a hotel for a holiday, but it can be a restful break from the busy everyday routine. *Too* restful, as some patients find when their seizures stop or diminish—at the very time when it would be helpful to have them! Because of this, the doctors reduce the patients' anti-epileptic medication once they are safely in hospital. This is an effective way of allowing seizures to occur—for a purpose, and in a controlled environment.

Central to the testing program is the SPECT or Ceretec test. If successful, this is a superb indicator of the source of the seizures. As soon as a seizure begins, you (or an observer) press a buzzer. The doctor entrusted with the Ceretec has only a minute or so to reach you and inject this radioactive substance into your bloodstream. The Ceretec 'lights up' the path of blood as it rushes to one part of the brain during a seizure, revealing what doctors—in a rare burst of poeticism—call a 'golden orb' on the image produced by the SPECT machine. After having Ceretec injected, you are taken to the nuclear medicine department for photographs. This process is repeated at a later stage when doctors believe that there is no epileptic activity in the brain and hence the images can be compared.

Most patients are so pleased to have 'performed' that they don't object to any of this, since a successful Ceretec test generally means release from the monitoring room. One activity which breaks the monotony of the days in the monitoring room is the neuro-psychological testing, or 'memory tests' as most patients call them. Both sides of the brain have their particular functions—put rather simplistically, the right side (in right-handed people) is concerned with non-verbal or visual memory including spatial relationships and the left side is concerned with language and verbal memory.

Functioning of the right side is tested with mazes and jigsaws, as well as reproducing detailed drawings which you've copied a short while before. The left side is tested with long lists of words and whole stories to be remembered. One of the most difficult things for me was having to recall which of the twenty 'pairs' of photographs of extraordinarily dull-looking men I'd seen before. This and an electronic maze gave me the most trouble while I breezed through anything to do with words. I thought this might be because I'm an English teacher, with little talent in the visual arts—but no, it bore out the results of the EEG, the video-monitoring and the Ceretec test: there was trouble in the right temporal lobe area of my brain.

I considered myself fortunate to have such a clear indication of what was going on, as I'd heard of other procedures which doctors sometimes use if uncertain about which side of the brain is impairing memory. The first is a direct implantation of electrodes into the temple, two at either side of the head, to allow a better EEG reading. 'Robyn', a fellow patient, had to have these tests a couple of times before the doctors had enough information to recommend surgery; she described the wires as 'a nuisance', but not painful.

The second is called a Wada test. An injection of a short-acting barbiturate called Amytal is made into the carotid artery via a catheter tube inserted into the femoral artery in the groin, effectively anaesthetising one hemisphere of the brain. The patient remains conscious and can thus be given memory tests, with literally only half a brain active. If the wakeful part of the brain is the one causing trouble, it should become very evident in this situation.

These tests may sound like something out of a sci-fi film but if you have the impression that the testing period in the monitoring room is a time of high drama, or as active as a soap opera, then you are mistaken. Most patients spend their time watching television, chatting to hospital staff, playing cards with visitors, and waiting, waiting, waiting for something to happen.

I was in the monitoring room for an exceptionally short time and was fortunate enough to need only one stay in hospital for the purpose. Most people undergo much longer stretches and many say that their time in the monitoring room was the worst part of the whole experience, surgery included, not because it is painful but because it can be very tedious. How keen one is to have surgery clearly makes all the difference to how one accepts this.

And there's always the possibility that the tests will show that a temporal lobectomy is not an option. The epilepsy may not clearly emanate from one temporal lobe or the operation may present too great a risk of impairment to functions such as sight or memory.

New technology like the PET machine will make it much easier in the future to assess an individual's suitability for epilepsy surgery. Because it gives such a detailed image of the chemical workings of the brain, the PET should fairly quickly locate the lesion or other problem causing a focal (or partial) epilepsy.

Furthermore, it may take only a couple of hours in an outpatients area, rather than admission to the hospital, to obtain the necessary information. Medical staff quite rightly point to this great advantage for all concerned as going a long way to justifying the cost of the PET machine. Perhaps one day the 'monitoring room' will be a thing of the past!

My tests had proved successful and in consultation with the family

I agreed to go ahead with surgery. Four months later, I was in theatre undergoing a temporal lobectomy, which involved removing about four centimetres of the anterior temporal lobe, including three centimetres of the hippocampus.

The procedure took about three or four hours, and I woke later that day in the recovery room. It is important to revive the patient as soon as possible and to check that vision—as well as 'brain power'— has not been impaired. I drifted in and out of consciousness, with mixed feelings about the oxygen mask. The pain in my head was not as fearful as I'd expected.

Nurses came with pills and a welcome cup of tea, doctors emerged through the blackness, asked questions—'Where are you?' 'Who is the Prime Minister?' 'Do you understand what has happened to you?'— and smiled, then disappeared. That night I was able to talk coherently with my doctor, who told me that they had found what they expected—scar tissue—had taken it out and that there had been no complications. It was likely that the infantile convulsions I'd reported to them were responsible for the scar on my right temporal lobe— fortunate perhaps that it had happened so early in childhood, since the brain had simply transferred certain functions to other parts of the brain.

Like most patients, I was up and about—although rather slowly— from about the second day, just for visits to the bathroom. Cleaning my teeth felt luxurious—but I avoided the bathroom mirror, too chicken to look at my partly shaven head with its 'question mark' wound held together by staples. I knew one side of my face was swollen and bruised, the bruises changing colour each day. In my opinion this was not the best time for taking family photographs but many patients would disagree, judging from the number of flashes constantly popping in the surgical ward.

I had been warned about the headache and pain, which was worse at night. The two Panadeine Forte plus my usual Tegretol finally sent me off to sleep but I woke several times and was glad of more pain relief during the night. But as my hair sprouted back, so did my sense of well-being—and a conviction that my seizures had gone forever.

As for my brain, two days after the operation I tackled the cryptic crossword from the *Guardian Weekly*—and got it out, for only the second time in my life! A week later, with bad headaches and my still startling appearance the only evidence of recent neurosurgery, I was discharged. I understood well the passage from *A Leg to Stand On* in which Oliver Sacks writes of the feeling of release on leaving hospital: 'a world now made possible, instead of the shifting half-world of patienthood and confinement I had been in'.

Surgery is only one of the ways out of that shifting half-world, available only to a minority of people with epilepsy, and disappointing in some cases. But it can be a dramatic and exciting resolution of one's seizures which, far from impairing the brain, can offer a future full of new possibilities.

Free of seizures, I have enjoyed success with the writing career I always wanted. Jim, in north Queensland, can now drive a car and has taken his independence further by moving out of home; Max, in Perth, has added stage appearances to his rigorous schedule as a dance teacher; Robyn has the confidence to take care of her neighbour's children, even crossing Albury's busy roads.

And Anne, from New South Wales, came back from a study tour of the United States with the Australian College of Seniors just in time to sit for her first year uni exams in English Literature—'and I *passed*!', she wrote to me excitedly. 'It proves that my brain is in working condition, even though part of it is missing!'

Epilepsy surgery may not be a modern miracle, but it comes pretty close!

THE PERENNIAL QUEST

FOR THE

STAR OF BETHLEHEM

DAVID H. LEWIS

DAVID H. LEWIS is a non-theist with no invisible means of support! He writes on the history of insights and ideas.

Nearly every Christmas we get some new theory about the Star of Bethlehem and recent years have been no exception. Just before Christmas 1993, York Films put out a 'documentary' entitled *The Star of Bethlehem* which traced David Hughes of Sheffield University's quest to identify just which star this was. The previous year the magazine *New Scientist* ran an article by Nigel Henbest entitled 'Bethlehem's Star Attraction!' So let's make a slightly sceptical survey of these perennial star searches.

David Hughes set the tone of his film by speaking of distilling the facts from the glitz and Nigel Henbest declared that the Magi saw 'something much more remarkable' than merely Venus. They then went to extraordinary lengths to examine every possible candidate for this miraculous star, from supernovae to aurorae and from comets to conjunctions. First, however, they took a little detour to establish just when Jesus might have been born because neither of them believes it was 25 December of the year dot and they assume they must fit his birth in with a known astronomical phenomenon! As it turned out, they independently agreed that it was 7 BC because the most spectacular 'star' they could find was a triple conjunction of Jupiter and Saturn in that year. (This, of course, is neither singular nor strictly a star, but let's not nitpick!) While this was an interesting rediscovery of an idea proposed at least as long ago as 1603 by Kepler, the point of all this is that it represents a beautiful example of naturalisation. With their scientific pretensions both researchers show an implicit embarrassment about accepting something that was frankly described as miraculous in the texts and feel obliged to find something that we think could plausibly have happened! In other words, they uncritically accept that an implausible event happened but they then try to find a plausible way to explain it!

Unfortunately, this leads them into even deeper quicksands when we follow the implications of this approach. Now, instead of God simply conjuring up a star specially to order, as He surely could, we find that He has to modify His schedule for the birth of His only Son to fit in with the natural movements of the Solar System. This does rather reduce Him to the role of the man waiting for the number 9 bus, unless of course, He has programmed the motions of the Solar System to synchronise with the future birth of Jesus from its very inception! But even this carries some fairly disagreeable predestinarian implications which suggest that we are all merely automatons playing out our preordained roles and nothing we can do or say will ultimately alter our karma!

None of this troubled Messrs Hughes or Henbest for they cheerfully proceeded to fortify their theory with 'corroboration' from the Gospel of Luke who, Hughes says, 'takes up the story' to substantiate the date which he finally fixes as the 15 September 7 BC! Mr Henbest was not quite so specific and plumps for October, though he at least had the grace to admit that the Gospels 'are contradictory'. Neither of them recognises that few theologians now regard the Gospels as eyewitness accounts. We are therefore dealing with contradictory hearsay evidence written nearly a century after the alleged event!

Incidentally, if Jesus was born in 7 BC it means that we have already had the turning of the second millennium. Since this was supposed by some to be the moment of the apocalyptic cataclysm foretold with great glee in Revelations, we can thank our lucky stars we've apparently survived it!

Now although, as we have noted, they both blithely accept Matthew's information that there *was* a star, they seemed remarkably incurious about its subsequent behaviour. After leading the Wise Men westwards to Jerusalem (the natural line of apparent movement across the sky), this star suddenly turns south and indicates a particular house in Bethlehem! As theologian Raymond Brown remarks, this would have been 'a celestial phenomenon unparalleled in astronomical history' and yet no one but Matthew noticed it. It evoked no notice from any other biblical writer nor from Josephus the Jewish historian nor from any astronomers of the time—only Matthew!

And yet even Matthew is inconsistent for after the star has led the Magi to Jerusalem (we don't ask why it didn't draw a whole horde of Magi from the East, like a celestial Pied Piper) Herod's advisers simply look up the appropriate prophecy in the scriptures and point them south to Bethlehem! (One is tempted to draw a comparison between this use of scriptures and an A–Z street directory, but we won't.) Thus miraculously rearranging the rhythm of the whole cosmos to turn this star southwards becomes quite unnecessary! If God can so readily divert a star from its natural course (or even create a special one), one wonders why He then allowed Herod to be such an inconvenient threat to the infant Jesus, forcing the family to flee to Egypt and slaughtering the unfortunate innocents. At one moment He facilitates His plans by miracles on a cosmic scale, but the next He is almost thwarted by a petty despot. Even this indiscriminate massacre defies reason because one wonders how hard it would have been for Herod to find a particular house in a small village that was pointed out by a star and which had been recently visited by exotic foreigners!

Equally strange is that nothing in Matthew's or Luke's later testimonies presupposes Jesus's extraordinary origins. Even though Jesus was born in this blaze of glory, by Matthew 14:1–2, Herod's son shows a blank incomprehension of who he is and his local community obviously regard him as a familiar but totally undistinguished citizen whose wisdom and mighty works take them completely by surprise (Matthew 13:54–6). Luke loses the plot even earlier because by Luke 2:48–50 Mary has so forgotten the import of her visitations by the Angel Gabriel and the Holy Spirit which 'came upon her' that she cannot understand why her twelve-year-old son has stayed at the temple to amaze the elders with his precocious wisdom. This doesn't ring true from a woman who has been told by an archangel that she will be impregnated by the Holy Ghost and her son will rule on the throne of David forever! These rather crass contradictions become a bit more intelligible when we remember that the Gospel writers were not recording personal reminiscences but rather clumsily blending together a number of diverse traditions.

But back to our intrepid researchers struggling through those theological quicksands! What conclusions do they draw from all this? Despite their imaginative speculations about Zoroastrian priests and ancient astrological lore, they are obviously not totally convinced by their own arguments. They both admit to some puzzlement at the whole paradox and though Mr Henbest wistfully wonders if it wasn't a miracle after all, in the end they leave their escape route open with a passing concession that Matthew might simply have made it all up!

Now at last we're getting somewhere! Now warning bells about Ockham's razor should be tinkling! Now at last we're doing what we should have done in the very first place—establishing the credentials of our witness. If someone reports a UFO sighting we naturally ask several basic questions. Was this an eyewitness sighting or is it a hearsay report? Did any one else witness it? When did it happen? What happened? Where? What happened next? From those questions we might make some inferences about the witness's credibility and consistency and we can assess the probability that there was in fact an actual sighting.

Messrs Hughes and Henbest have come at the question from the other direction entirely. They have assumed from the first that there must have been a UFO (or a U stellar O) because Matthew said so and they then moved heaven and Earth to find it! Only when their fruitless quest leads them almost full circle does it occur to them that they might have been going the wrong way!

Never mind, it was an interesting academic astronomical exercise but if they want a real challenge may I suggest they turn their attention to Joshua 10:12–15. Here, at Joshua's command 'The Sun stood still and the moon did not move . . . in the middle of the sky and did not go down for a whole day' which enabled Joshua to defeat his foes at the battle of Aijalon. (He also had a little help from giant hailstones which killed large numbers of the unfortunate Amorites but apparently missed his own men following in hot pursuit!)

One thing at a time, however. Let's take the astronomical miracle first. We have corroboration of the story in the Book of Jashar and from modern astronomical knowledge we realise that in fact it must not have been the sun and the moon that stood still in the sky but the Earth itself screeching to a stop. The world stopped turning on its axis! As theologian Bernard Ramm calmly remarked 'the disturbances on the Earth and the Solar System would have been enormous' and presumably there should be some record of these effects. So as a change from the perennial quest for the Star of Bethlehem, let's have some enterprising astronomers explaining how 'the sun stood still . . . for a whole day'!

KEEPING PEOPLE IN CAGES

PETER MACINNIS

PETER MACINNIS has stopped changing professions and continues to teach boys how to use computers and how to communicate at St Paul's College, Manly, a Sydney suburb.

People often have trouble trying to pin down my profession. Indeed, I sometimes have trouble defining that myself. Every two or three years I change, moving on to new horizons, or moving back to old ones. You see, there are quite a few things I enjoy doing, and I believe in seeking out jobs that will let me do as many of them as possible. Mainly, I enjoy anything to do with the sciences, teaching young people, messing about with computers, and writing. Most of my moves have been associated with a varying urge to concentrate on one or another of these four interests.

For three years I was at the Australian Museum in Sydney, but now I've returned to classroom teaching. I've got my *own* students, and the chance to watch them develop under my guidance. I'm teaching Computing Studies, introducing students to the effective use of the computer as a means to higher ends, rather than as an end in itself.

As part of this, I've been teaching my Year 9 students to write on the word processor. They've been taught to write in a certain way by their English teachers, and now I'm teaching them an entirely different method. The word processor is a useful tool for writing, but only once you realise that it's neither a pen and paper, nor even a typewriter. It requires a very different approach to planning, drafting and writing.

The boys are writing news stories about local events for a network called Global Village News, part of a worldwide educational network called K12Net. When their stories are ready, we send them by modem to a local centre. Within a day, that centre connects with other centres around the world, and our stories trickle through at off-peak rates. Students in the United States, New Zealand, Germany, Canada, South Africa, Aruba and beyond, can read our stories, just as we read theirs.

Several of the boys independently decided to tell the story of a man who died in the Corso, the main street of Manly, just down the hill from our school. The man's body lay on the street for a considerable time before anybody realised the man was dead. 'We thought he was just sleeping it off,' people said. The man was apparently a heavy drinker. One of my students was appalled at what seemed to be a complete lack of attention or compassion from the passers-by. 'How could people do it?' he asked me. 'How could people be so uncaring, so lacking in curiosity?'

'People,' I assured him, 'are capable of ignoring many strange and curious things.' School was over, and a few students had stayed behind to finish things off. As we were in our own time, I sat down to reminisce about the time I kept and displayed two savages in a cage at the Australian Museum.

It was late 1992, and everybody was busy doing last-minute Christmas shopping, and the Sydney Biennale was on as well, so it was hardly surprising my students had missed the visit to Sydney of two colourful savages from Guatinau, a recently discovered island in the Caribbean. Coincidentally, I said, the visiting display reached us in the week of the bicentenary of Bennelong and Yammerawannie being taken off to London to be shown to King George III. 'Who was Yammerawannie?' they asked.

He was, I explained, the less successful exhibit, dying of pneumonia in Britain, and so never returning to his native shore like Bennelong. Still, I added, King George liked them. It probably made a change for George from being an exhibit himself.

'Because he was a Royal?' one of them asked.

'Because he was mad,' I replied. 'People used to go to Bedlam, the insane asylum, to laugh at the inmates, and a mad king was even more fun. People used to say that when George had an argument with a tree, the tree usually won.'

They tittered dutifully, but one of them looked thoughtful. 'I'm glad we don't go in for that sort of thing today . . . '

'True,' I said, 'but we *do* accept displaying savages in a cage. Nobody gets upset by *that*, or not in my experience.' Then I told them how our two outrageously colourful Guatinaui were displayed in a golden cage at the Australian Museum for three days.

I was open with my students from the start that the display was a hoax. It was a Biennale event, undertaken by two performance artists, intended to provoke a public reaction, but so far as the Australian public was concerned, the 'Year of the White Bear' was the genuine article. Like any good hoax, *everything* was over the top, so the more perceptive could see through our hoax, but at no time would we *admit* that it was anything other than genuine.

At the end of 1992, the International Year for the World's Indigenous Peoples was just a few days away from its start, and three young Koori men took it in turns to watch over us, ready to intervene if anybody became too worked up about our display, but their presence was never needed. Nobody, *but nobody*, objected.

The 'savages' were two American performance artists, Coco Fusco and Guillermo Gomez-Pena. I first heard of them on a Radio National program in mid 1992, talking about people's racial stereotypes, and how they, as Latinos, were perceived and depicted by Hollywood and Anglo-America generally, and what it was like to be inside the cage.

When I heard they were coming to the museum, I volunteered to be one of the guards outside the cage. It was a role requiring a storyteller with a consummate flair for telling lies and tall tales with a straight face, I said. The museum management accepted my offer unflatteringly quickly. They also accepted an American lady who was working as a volunteer in the museum's Arachnology section.

Coco and Guillermo wore, when on display, swimming costumes, sneakers and sunglasses, while she had a wig and yellow face paint, and he wore a Mexican wrestler's mask. They both wore collars, to which we would attach a dog-chain when they left the cage ('for their own safety', we would explain officiously). They added various bits and pieces to the kit, but that was their basic ensemble. It was more than enough to make them unrecognisable when they went out at night, or when Coco spoke on radio as an 'anthropologist' travelling with the specimens.

Inside the cage, Coco and Guillermo didn't communicate with the public, and so were free to observe public reactions from behind their dark glasses. The guards, on the other hand, were to present the public face of the display. The 'savages' spoke no English, but they could communicate with us by sign language. If they wanted to hear a conversation with a visitor, they would signal to be fed, and we would then handfeed them with fruit while continuing the conversation.

If they wanted to brief us, they would signal to be taken to the toilet, and then talk to us outside, before we led them back to the cage. Most of *my* instructions came from Guillermo, who kept demanding 'Be more aggressive! Provoke them!'. We were calculatedly provocative and patronising in all our comments and actions, but to little effect.

As 'guards', we were dressed in white overalls and dark glasses. We presented as two enthusiastic but untrained people who'd picked up a certain amount of hearsay information, and who knew the general details. If pressed, we'd encourage the visitor to read the text displayed in front of the cage. We were, we would say, just the guards, and the anthropologists who had *all* the answers were away at that time.

If attacked by unbelievers, and there were some, we'd simply say something like 'I can assure you, sir (or madam) that the Guatinaui are just as genuine as their island, and you can see *that* on the map over *there.*' Confronted with impressive cartographic evidence, allegedly from the *Encyclopaedia Britannica*, most doubters were effectively silenced. (One of these days I'm going to make a fortune selling Harbour Bridges to Sydneysiders.) If somebody asked why the Guatinaui were wearing sunglasses, or sneakers, or why the male specimen was wearing surf shorts, Coco and Guillermo told us to say simply that theirs was a syncretic culture which happily absorbed all sorts of elements from other cultures.

As to how they'd collected so much 'outside' material while remaining undiscovered and unspoiled, that was left for me to explain. It was, I'd say, gesturing around the map, a result of the interplay between circumpolar effects derived from the Gulf Stream and an intermittent form of inadvertent Coriolis forces. Clearly, I would conclude, this would result in currents going towards the island, but never away, so that drifting objects and castaways might be carried there, but nobody could ever leave. Faced with such a wealth of technical detail, most questioners wisely fled.

The last display day was the Saturday before Christmas, and the crowds were light around lunchtime. Our specimens decided that we should take them for a walk through the busy shops, and down to the Art Gallery. We did so, but to almost no reaction. In the end all we got was somebody saying *that* was what he wanted to wear to the party, and a lady spruiking into a microphone outside a bookshop asked what we were selling. When I explained that these were two savages who were on display in the Australian Museum and getting some fresh air, she told the crowd about this, straight-faced, but once again, nobody twitched or looked shocked. Sydneysiders are *so* cool.

Outside the cage, we always had the 'Biennale crowd', an in-group who came to watch the public being fooled, and who were all *so* ultra-cool about their own heightened awareness. Once, I launched into an impassioned speech about how we had hopes that the savages would, in the fullness of time, given their natural sense of rhythm, become civilised like us, and go out and capture their own savages to put in cages. I put everything into it, playing to my audience, trying to make them crack up, as they'd been doing to me. I finished on a high note, and found, too late, an elderly couple in the audience, clearly *not* part of the Biennale push. But I needn't have worried. Seeing me looking in their direction, they beamed their appreciation of what we were doing in helping the savages to rise to that level. Nothing, *but nothing*, upsets the Australian public!

One curious feature was people's prurient interest in whether or not the savages would 'do it' in the cage, and whether they slept there at night. I would reply blandly, that no, the savages were quite civilised, and that they slept in a padded room out the back in complete privacy, apart from the one-way mirror and three video cameras. Even *that* offended nobody!

One of the 'givens' of quaint natives everywhere is that they are colourful, they tell amusing legends, and they dance exotic dances. Our specimens were prepared to pose for a photo with the public, using their own Polaroid camera for one dollar. For the same fee, the female would perform an exotic dance to tribal rap music, or the male specimen would tell a story in his language about one of the totemic objects that he kept in a black briefcase which had syncretically become part of his culture.

One of my students asked if we still cage people. No, we don't put genuine savages in cages any more, I said. Not because we're more civilised, but rather more because we can go on tours and see the natives in their native habitats, or we can sit at home and have them displayed upon our television screens in all their quaintness.

But if we *did* still show off exotic people in cages, would we worry about it? I'm not sure, after hearing Paul Berents describing last year just how willingly we whites accepted the actions of the so-called Aborigines' Protection Board, right up until 1969, effectively abducting children and fostering them out to 'more civilised' white families. After that, I could believe almost anything of modern Australian society.

One of the boys suggested that it might have been like that in Nazi Germany, that this might explain the events he'd seen depicted in *Schindler's List*. I still prefer to think we had an audience who mostly saw the hoax for what it was, and played along with our piece of theatre. But I *know* there were also those who accepted all they heard and saw completely. It worried me, I said.

'And when it was all over,' asked one of them, 'what did it all prove?'

'Not a great deal,' I had to confess. Maybe it showed that we, as a culture, are prepared to accept all sorts of things, so long as they don't threaten our personal comfort. Australians were far more willing to accept this sort of behaviour than American and Spanish cultures.

'But what did Coco and Guillermo make of it all?' he persisted.

'I've no idea,' I answered. 'You see, by the time we got round to evaluating the experience, Coco and Guillermo had taken off to savour the quaint and exotic natives of Bali, in their local habitat.'

WILL POLIO BE THE SECOND DISEASE TO BE ERADICATED FROM THE FACE OF THE EARTH?

ANTHONY RADFORD

Emeritus Professor ANTHONY RADFORD, formerly Foundation Professor of Primary Care and Community Medicine at South Australia's Flinders University, is a consultant in public and international health.

What was the first? Yes, smallpox. The last person who caught smallpox 'in the wild' was a man in Ethiopia in 1978. And polio will most likely be the second disease to go into the bin marked 'No Longer Exists'.

If there were two cases of poliomyelitis this year in Australia, the public would be beating a path to the door of the Department of Health in outcry at 'this epidemic of polio'. When I started medicine in the mid 1950s, if there had been only two cases a quarter, people would have said, 'Where has all the polio gone?'. An epidemic is when 'more than the usual number of cases of a disease occurs in a given population over a given time'.

Polio has, in recent years, raised its ugly head again in Australia in the form of what is called the Post Polio Syndrome. This is a condition in which old polio survivors find, among other things, that their affected limbs are becoming a little weaker again. But that is not the topic of this piece. The usual number of new cases of polio in Australia is now zero. There hasn't been a proven new case in this country since 1986. However, because there is still a significant number of children who are not fully immunised, the risk of its reappearance still exists. But maybe not for much longer.

Poliomyelitis, or infantile paralysis as it used to be known, is caused by one of three related viruses, named Polio 1, 2 and 3. They occur only in humans and are usually transmitted from one person to another by what is known as the faeco-oral route, that is, through ingestion of contaminated food or water from infected persons to susceptible or non-immune persons.

Polio has been around for a long time. We know from rock engravings that even the pharaohs of Egypt were not immune. Indeed, they were more likely to suffer from the serious ill effects of the disease than others. Why? Because the older one is when infected with polio virus, the more likely you are to get the paralytic complications. Because the water supply in the palace was of better quality than that of the masses it was less likely to become contaminated with wild polio virus, and so the young pharaoh was more likely to get any infection much later than the majority of his subjects.

In many developing countries, before immunisation programs got under way, often over 90 per cent of children were infected with polio virus by the time they reached their fifth birthday. However, only between three and seven in every thousand suffered residual lameness. We know this by studying the presence of antibodies, those proteins measurable in the bloodstream and specific for each germ and which indicate earlier infection, and by what are called lameness surveys.

Normally, when someone is infected with polio, the germ, which is a virus, enters the body through the mouth and intestine, hence it is called an entero-virus. Once inside the body it causes a flu-like illness with fever, headache, sore throat and muscle aches and pains. In a small number of people the virus comes to rest in nervous cell tissue, especially the grey cells of the spinal cord or brain, hence it is also called a neurotropic virus. These grey cells control muscle movements. When they are inflamed or killed by the virus, weakness or paralysis occurs.

If the infected cells don't recover, permanent weakness may result if the remaining muscles are not able to expand and take over the work of the cells that have died. Sometimes quite disabling contractures result, especially of the hands and arms. If the cells of the muscles which are involved with breathing or swallowing are affected in the acute process, death may result or survival may only be possible with a respirator. Several decades ago these respirators were called 'iron lungs'. The patient was placed in a huge box like a coffin. Then, by alternating positive and negative pressures inside the box, the equipment was able to pull out and push in the chest wall and so breathe for you.

Before immunisation was available, each year more than half a million people, mainly children, suffered residual paralysis from the effects of polio, and in excess of 50 000 died. In the early 1950s Dr Jonas Salk developed a vaccine against the polio virus using killed strains of virus. This form of the vaccine had to be injected. A few years later Dr Albert Sabin, also from the United States, developed a vaccine from weakened but still live virus, but which could be taken by mouth, and was therefore easier to give and more pleasant to receive. The vaccine is given as drops placed under the tongue. The oral form unfortunately causes very occasional cases of paralysis—but less commonly than one in a million doses. However, by being given by mouth the lining cells of the intestine are infected, make antibodies and so help prevent spread of the wild virus.

In 1976 the World Health Organisation—joined later by UNICEF—launched an international program of childhood immunisation for six diseases including polio. The others were BCG against tuberculosis, DPT—or Triple Antigen as we often call it in Australia—against diphtheria, pertussis and tetanus, and measles. The Save the Children Fund had already launched its own campaign to Stop-Polio, and later Rotary International gave its support through its Polio-Plus project through which it aimed to celebrate its centenary year of 2002 with a declaration of the global eradication of poliomyelitis.

WHO and UNICEF have set a target of global eradication of polio by the year 2000, as part of the world program of Health for All by 2000. And we are well on the way. Partly because the immunisation coverage is so good in the thirty-five countries of this part of the world, known as the Western Pacific Region of WHO, or WPRO for short, only four countries in the region were still reporting poliomyelitis at the beginning of 1995—China, Laos, Vietnam and Cambodia. Papua New Guinea and Malaysia were on the list but no cases have been proven in either country for more than three years.

I was one of a six-member committee known as the WPRO TAG for EPI and PEI, an acronym for quite a mouthful—the Western Pacific Region Technical Advisory Group for the Expanded Program on Immunisation and the Polio Eradication Initiative. This group meets once or twice a year in one of the countries where polio is still endemic, that means, where the disease still occurs, to review progress towards eradication.

With much improved surveillance mechanisms, and in the case of Papua New Guinea a financial reward for anyone reporting a case which proves to be polio, the numbers are going down each year. In 1980 there were over 12 000 reports, in 1991 it was down to 2600 and in 1992 the number dipped below 2000. Not surprisingly, most cases are being reported from China, with Vietnam showing the next highest rate. Each endemic country has mounted what seems like a massive military operation to mop-up the remaining pockets of the disease by investigating every reported case, and striving to ensure the highest possible levels of immunisation in young children. At the end of 1994, 80 million Chinese children were immunised over two days—probably the greatest single public health action the world has ever seen.

Some quite ingenious activities have been devised to assist in increasing the coverage rates of immunisation. Heads of state have been enlisted to launch National Immunisation Days and have been publicised giving the first dose of the campaign. For example, once, when helping to conduct a National Immunisation Week in Papua New Guinea, the former nutritionist wife of the Prime Minister and the Governor-General agreed to launch the campaign by giving the first doses. Another example of innovation is where school children have been taught how to check immunisation records as part of a school community project and are then made responsible for checking the houses nearest theirs to see if any young children are not up to date. If they find any such children they encourage the mothers to attend the next clinic—a process called social mobilisation.

Coverage with vaccine, which is known as OPV—Oral Polio Vaccine—is higher in the Western Pacific Region than in any other of the five WHO regions of the globe. Over 90 per cent of children are now immunised by their first birthday in this part of the world and we were going for a target of 95 per cent coverage by 1995. Data is still not in as to how close we are to achieving this target. The hardest task is for nations to maintain this level which will be required till all regions have reported no single case for several years.

Regrettably, there are still many children in Australia who have not yet been fully immunised. Thus the risk of infection continues. Some countries, and now the ACT, Victoria and New South Wales in Australia, require evidence of immunisation before admission to pre-school, kindergarten or primary school. Others require the basic immunisation program to be completed by a certain age before family allowances can be claimed. Whatever the method, immunisation rates continue to rise and disease reports fall.

Yes. There is every chance that poliomyelitis will be the second disease to be banished from the face of the Earth.

SOIL IMPROVEMENT—THE STEP
BEYOND CONSERVATION

BARRIE OLDFIELD

**BARRIE OLDFIELD is an environmental film maker
and President of Men of The Trees in Western
Australia.**

On 10 June 1992 what is technically known as 'a wind event' occurred
in the wheat-belt of Western Australia.

Strong winds always seem to blow in this part of the world. But
on this particular morning they were really becoming uncomfortable.
By late morning whisps of soil from paddocks which had been dry
seeded were lifting like mares' tails. By midday the whole paddock
took off. Within a few minutes friends just a few paces away
became like grey smudges. The stinging sand caused us to turn
away from the wind. The distant house, its white walls picked up
in the sunlight, shone eerily in the grey cloud with no distinct
ground to stand on.

What made this dust storm a little different from most was that the
winds carried much of it away towards the coast and to Perth. That
afternoon the people of Perth were treated to an experience of the
wheat-belt they were not expecting. Instead of rain the cloud precipitated dust on the city. Then, without stopping, away it went across

the coast to dump its precious load in the Indian Ocean where it's of absolutely no use to anyone.

A month or two later, on that same farm, my attention was drawn to the bank of soil against the fence. All farmers have come to recognise this. Fences act as soil traps and eventually become completely buried. On this occasion there was still 40 centimetres or so of fence visible where a full metre should have stood to contain the sheep. I took a spade and cut a transect down to the original ground level against one fence post. And there revealed, like a digging on some archaeological site, was a sad history of no less than five such storms—all in the period of the life of that fence. After each storm grasses and weeds had grown. Then along had come the dust and covered them with a few more centimetres. Then the grasses and weeds had grown again. Quite distinctly visible were five layers of dark organic material laid down in this transect which could have spanned no more than twenty years.

Of course this is the main reason Australians are planting trees. Trees by the millions. Only trees and shrubs planted in well-designed shelter belts will lift those winds above ground level and protect the soil. And one of the good things that is happening is that, as a nation, we are becoming very good at planting trees and getting them to grow well. There is quite a challenge in planting out a tiny seedling, no more than 20 centimetres high, in our semi-arid wheat-belt and expecting it not only to survive but to grow well without further attention. Yet here, on another farm, so far to the fringe of agriculture that beyond the fence you drop off the edge of the world, trees planted in the winter of one year stand head high the next!

Of course this experience and skill has to be learned. It comes from actually doing the work, of going beyond the trivial garden or parkland planting and getting right out there where the farms are big, the roads are gravel, and where the hospitality really glows. And that's where you'll find this positive group, the Men of The Trees, showing their style.

For a number of years now this Society has looked very closely at what factors are essential for tree survival. Its members have spent collectively thousands of hours developing techniques for reforesting arid land, making sure they do not have to go back to the same site twice by getting the planting right in the first place.

Attention to the trees has paid off handsomely. But those soils, with nothing in them to bind them together, with nothing for next year's crop other than a pinch of highly soluble fertiliser, have now attracted the attention of the curious. It is not good enough simply to conserve these soils. And so a new phrase has entered the conversation of Men of The Trees in Western Australia—*soil improvement.*

While Australia is talking about 'Landcare' and 'Soil Conservation' this dirt-under-the-fingernails Society is already working towards the idea that we have to do much better than just protecting the soils of our land. We have to start *rebuilding* them, *rejuvenating* them, making them infinitely more vital than they were even before white man came to Terra Australis Incognita and cleared the bush to grow crops. And that is a very different matter indeed.

ROCK DUST—REMINERALISATION

In March 1989 I visited the island of Nauru to make a film with television ecologist David Bellamy. Of course our conversations ranged widely over the management of the Earth's resources, the practice of the Law of Return, the need of humanity for the products of a healthy biosphere, and the interdependence of all life, including ours, on the protection of natural living systems. On the night we arrived back in Melbourne I had arranged to meet with Vernon G. Lawrence AM of Hawthorn. Vern Lawrence, a retired farmer, publishes an occasional newsletter *Humus and Rock.* We discussed remineralisation.

Now the theory of remineralisation runs like this. Every 100 000 years or so the Earth goes through a complete cycle of ice age followed by a warmer period, the interglacial. This cycle has happened a number of times over the past million years or more. During the periods of glaciation, great glaciers cover much of the higher latitudes. The weight and movement of the ice grinds down the surface rock of the earth so that when the ice finally recedes a great wealth of newly ground mineral material is available as the foundation for new soils.

These minerals, together with humus, form the basis for a resilient, highly nutritious soil which is rapidly colonised by billions upon billions of micro-organisms. So many organisms in fact that scientists estimate that the mass of these living organisms below ground level is possibly five times the mass of all life above the soil.

Nor was this idea of remineralisation in any way new. Way back in the 1890s a German agronomist by the name of Julius Henzel had discovered that applications of rock dust to agricultural soils resulted in healthier plants and healthier animals and people who fed on them. This idea of Henzel's has never really lost currency. Today, throughout much of Germany, Austria and Switzerland the word *Gesteinsmehl* is everywhere seen and accepted as great truck-tankers of rock dust, with huge cannons mounted on the back, blast their life-restoring load into the highly stressed forests, bringing back life to trees that once looked doomed by acid rain.

It was then that I felt that Men of The Trees had a clear run—a promising avenue of research that seemed to point to a healthier soil environment for the better establishment of trees. Furthermore, the act of soil rejuvenation would have implications for the whole farming industry, in particular the diversification of the farm product through new crops and management techniques including agriforestry in its broadest sense.

ROCK DUST TRIAL RESULTS

Two seasons of trials were conducted on a broadly scattered basis. Approximately seventy people, most of them living close to Perth, undertook to dedicate a 4 square metre plot to the research. In addition, two students of biology at Curtin University, working under the direction of Dr John Fox, did some quantitative field trials. At the end of the two seasons results were somewhat inconclusive, yet a golden thread was emerging which became the guide for a limited trial at the Men of The Trees nursery at St Barbe Grove, in Hazelmere.

The results of this trial were outstanding. In seven weeks beneficial results were clearly seen. Press and television news followed and many inquiries were received. The pathway to further broadscale field trials opened up. In close succession came the opportunity to take up 23 hectares of typical wheat-growing country in the shire of Dowerin and the first substantial backing from a local quarry which agreed to supply the rock dust for the venture. But the most encouraging support of all came from many gifts from ordinary people, all over Australia, people who simply wanted the work to succeed.

Users of rock dust believe (although they cannot yet prove scientifically) that rock dust works through offering microbial access to its clean cut face rather than as a soluble fertiliser might do through ionic action. The dust creates a large surface area of freshly cut granite which seems to encourage the vigour of soil micro-organisms. These smallest of living cells create great interlocking communities, other organisms living off the decaying residues of the prime 'rock eaters'. Eventually, through endless food chains linking rock, humus, bacteria, algae, lichens, yeasts, the dark side of a truly living soil gives consent for the growth of a healthy plant and animal life above it. That is simply the theory. There is much detailed analytical work to be done and Men of The Trees can only open the doors to new research. Nevertheless, our observations are based upon actually doing the work in soils with living plant—and with 'dirt under the fingernails'.

Within eight weeks of the start of the rainy season and the opening of the trial farm, we had planted 11 000 trees. Faced with the soils of Dowerin, shallow tilth, deep compacted clay subsoil with a pH of 4.9

to 5.4, and with very little to go on by way of relevant experience, we made some quick and arbitrary decisions.

We eventually got the clay ripped to one metre depth using a D8 bulldozer. The D6 simply had not got the weight. Into the rip line we sank a tractor-mounted auger, pulverising the clay to the full depth of the rip. But the auger also worked like a food blender, the perfect tool for taking the 7 kilograms or so of dampened granite dust down into the subsoil at each planting site. We had struck lucky. Our first attempt at handling this difficult material and introducing it at depth to the soil seemed to be working well.

The late season was also on our side. With domestic matters to attend to, such as the official opening and ceremonial flypast, we could not get onto the land until mid-June. And our first day out coincided with a horrendous dust storm. Just the experience we needed to reinforce our resolve to plant trees to protect this precious land!

But the dry start to winter gave us a clay that crumbled rather than sealed off under the thrust of the auger so we were able to prevent the sides of each hole from becoming glazed and difficult for tree roots to penetrate. As each hole was prepared it was topped off with a spadeful of composted animal manure by courtesy of Perth Zoo, a little more rock dust, and the top soil. So far as we were able, each seedling was mulched—newspapers, old carpet, lawn clippings. No wheat-belt planted tree seedlings ever had a better start!

THE IMPLICATIONS FOR OUR NATIVE PLANTS

Many times I have returned to sites of our former tree plantings. Whilst we give the tree seedlings the very best start possible—deep ripping, fertilisation, weed control—the most vigorous growth occurs where the soil still retains something of its former 'self'. Soil is a very complex material. Its vital constituents and structure are made by living organisms.

An early indication that remineralisation might work for natural regrowth was seen on the site of an old metal dump at Nukarni way to the east of the Western Australian wheat-belt. Again, this was just one of those fragments one stores away in the mind in case it should connect with future experience.

As harvest comes around students from Curtin and Edith Cowan universities are carrying out quantitative observations to guide the farm planning for next year.

Western civilisation learned its agriculture trade on the young, resilient, glacial soils of England and northern Europe. When that style of cultivation was brought to other parts of the world, all kinds of problems arose. And now, in Australia, we face a herculean task to put things to right as we tackle landcare in this last decade of the century.

We are not talking 'soil conservation' any more. We are talking 'soil improvement', and that is something that civilisation has never really attended to since the Sumerians bequeathed their worn-out agricultural plains to the Babylonians. The land that is now the gibber desert of the Middle East.

I hope that many will contribute to this work so that millions may benefit from what we learn. To me the world is a precious gift beyond belief. That we should take a purely exploitive attitude is now incomprehensible. Certainly there are two factors, time and money, which we must always take into account. But the great advantage of working with a dedicated Society of volunteers such as Men of The Trees is that we can put these factors in their rightful priority. They are on our list, but not at the top of it.

SCIENTISTS BEWARE:
ANTI-SCIENCE IS CREEPING
UP ON YOU!

PETER POCKLEY

**PETER POCKLEY is a science writer and broadcaster
and a former head of the ABC's Science Unit.**

Scientists are fond of telling 'horror stories' of misinterpretation of their work, especially in headlines, but, as I see it, most reports in the mainstream media of Australia are reasonably accurate and supportive of science. As those of us in the thick of it know well—whether we're scientists, writers or broadcasters—there's a huge, unmet demand by readers, listeners and viewers for stories soundly based on science.

My concern here, though, is with evidence that appreciation of the value of science—and trust in science—is waning in the community. And I'm concerned that too few scientists are recognising the trend and using their new-found skills at communication truly to *engage* with the public—not just to talk *at* them or to rely solely on the media.

There's an anti-science movement creeping up on scientists from several directions and it seems many of them are unaware of the danger this presents to the scientific enterprise and enlightenment which, more often than not, works for the benefit of humanity.

Formal education in science remains an integral part of all school experience and most Australians enjoy access to excellent museums and science centres. Despite these, and the presence of sound reports on science in the media, curious, weird and wonderful ideas about nature continue to be spawned and, when these surface in the popular media, it's been too easy to laugh them off as oddballs.

In the community at large there's an astonishing range and penetration of anti-scientific beliefs. For a start let's take 'alternative medicine' which, by and large, discards the achievements of research-based medicine, replacing it with trust in so-called 'healthy' or 'natural' remedies. According to the largest survey of its kind in the world, just concluded by Adelaide University, nearly half of Australia's population now consult alternative medical practitioners or use the remedies they promote.

Alastair MacLennan found that alternative medical practitioners and self-prescribed substances are worth a billion dollars a year in Australia—that's a substantial industry. He points out that few of the many remedies which are bought over the counter from so-called 'health shops' (and, increasingly, in pharmacies) have been subjected to the rigorous testing the *same* public expects of prescribed drugs and treatments from medicine based on research.

Among the public there is, dare I say it, a remarkable *faith* in alternatives, a faith backed by little more than anecdotes rather than the hard, testable evidence which is the very stuff of science. While the public is declaring, with its purse, a lack of trust in science and its institutions, the scientists and authorities working in conventional medicine have not taken the threat seriously enough to investigate the claims and to counter them with evidence.

Equally serious, perhaps, is the type of anti-science associated with the so-called New Age philosophies, the counter-culture and fundamentalism. Some prefer the stronger term of 'pseudo-science' with its implications of deliberate misinformation or intellectual fraud.

These belief systems exert a strong hold among our supposedly educated public and scientists have failed to debunk them comprehensively. Here's a short list. I present it in no priority order, just alphabetically:

Astrology and horoscopes—which get favoured placement in many mainstream newspapers and lifestyle magazines.

Auras—magically surrounding our bodies.

Channelling and clairvoyance—talking directly with the spirits of the dead.

Creationism—which rejects the record of fossils in the rocks and opposes teaching of Darwin's theory of evolution.

Crystal power—the belief that wearing a crystal of quartz has healing effects on the troubled body and mind and can make your wishes come true.

Divining for water with bent rods.

Extra-sensory perception, telepathy or mind-reading and other forms of parapsychology.

Extra-terrestrials or aliens visiting Earth and abducting humans.

Fortune-telling with horoscopes, numerology, Ouija boards, palmistry and Tarot cards.

Psychic powers such as spoon bending.

Psychic surgery—removing tumours by hand.

Pyramid powers—the influence today of ancient Egyptian beliefs.

Telekinesis—or moving things by power of the mind.

Unidentified Flying Objects, flying saucers and all that.

Now, some of these are harmless enough and some are confined to a few believers, but others are virtual cults or money-making industries. Commonly, they reflect aspects of counter-culture and we may label this significant segment of the anti-science movement more appropriately as 'counter-science', though the creationists are deeply religious people who promote their belief as 'creation *science*'.

Few Australian scientists have gone public about anti-science. The running has been left to concerned non-scientists like Harry Edwards, whose little volume on the subject is informative as a starting point. It's titled *Skeptoon—An Illustrated Look at Some New Age Beliefs.*

One Australian scientist taking the threat seriously is Ian Plimer, Professor of Geology in the University of Melbourne and winner of the 1995 Eureka Prize for Promotion of Science. He's particularly concerned with the creationists who teach youngsters that the story of Noah's Ark is absolute truth rather than symbolic. There are no half-truths—creationists dismiss two centuries of geologial science as total bunk.

While Plimer is attacking groups in the fundamentalist wing of religion, the anti-science movement is wider than this, and includes sections of academia which go so far as to assert scientific knowledge is only one of many ways of explaining how the physical world works.

Australia has yet to experience the full force of this intellectual attack on science on grounds of philosophy, ideology and morality which is evident overseas, notably in the United States. Scientists can get so involved in the excitement of their own investigations that they seldom hear the other side—the scepticism and, in some cases, the downright hostility being directed against both them and their science.

The intensive, focused training of scientists may also be a factor. With few exceptions scientists have dismissed the proponents of anti-science as living in irrational, imaginary worlds—they're treated as ill-informed or misguided or ill-educated or fruit loops. Yet, many of them *are* evidently well educated.

Publicity of scientific achievements through the media is a useful antidote but, by itself, it's inadequate. The scientific community has placed too many expectations in the power of the news to convey *understanding* to the wider public. The media remain important setters of agendas but they should not be taken for granted or treated as a mouthpiece for science—sufficient, constant and uncritical.

The scene in the press is mixed. Some papers have expanded their coverage of science while others have virtually dropped it.

What's behind this? It seems that the confidence scientists have placed in the media for changing public perceptions of science is being undermined. Some editors and program managers clearly show no debt to the very science underpinning the technology making possible their own industry of newspapers and radio and television. One popular paper has recently slashed its coverage of science to occasional snippets while it's kept space going for the totally unfounded predictions of horoscopes—in the late 1990s astrology has become resurgent over astronomy. Galileo turn in your grave!

The work of scientists is founded on centuries of well-documented tests showing that inanimate matter and life behave according to laws of nature and mathematical logic. When scientists get to know this predictability well enough, their basic research spins off into reliable applications.

As a result drivers expect cars to obey their commands, passengers expect aeroplanes to fly; and everybody expects telephones and computers and radio and television to work and for their food and drugs to be safely tested—all according to scientific principles.

For most scientists, then, it's quite perplexing to confront intelligent people who in their daily lives happily buy and apply these products of research but who, at the same time, disbelieve assurances of scientific demonstration. Science has yet to convey that research is never final, that it's full of surprises and so-called laws

and logic are continually refined through more experiment, observation and vigorous debate among researchers. This may be why
the nature of error and levels of risk are so imperfectly understood
by the public.

At the 1996 annual meeting of the American Association for the
Advancement of Science, Raymond Eve and fellow sociologists of
the University of Texas reported a growth in the numbers of anti-
scientists in the United States. Their survey found religious creationists and adherents of the New Age diverge in their views on issues
such as genetic engineering and abortion but they share a general
criticism of science, seeing it as the *cause* of spiritual decline. When
their claims are rejected by scientists they attribute it to 'dogmatism,
narrow-mindedness, lack of imagination or excessive conformity by
scientists'. Anti-scientists can be effective lobbyists, attracting coverage in the media and, according to Ray Eve, weakening public
support for science and encouraging politicians to keep the purse
strings tight.

In their book, *Higher Superstition*, Paul Gross, a biologist of the
University of Virginia, and Norman Levitt, a mathematician of
Rutgers University, describe the open hostility of what they call 'the
academic left' towards 'the *actual content* of scientific knowledge
and towards the assumption, which one might have supposed
amc ›g educated people, that scientific knowledge is reasonably
reliable and rests on a sound methodology . . . They accuse science
itself of a reactionary obscurantism, and they revile it as an ideo-
logical prop of the present order, which many of them despise and
hope to abolish'.

Gerald Holton, a physicist and historian of science at Harvard
University, in his book *Science and Anti-Science*, urges scientists to
recognise that their opponents entertain totally different world views
and to make an effort to comprehend and answer them, even if
they seem irrational.

The time has come, then, for scientists to become well informed about their critics and, in the process, to appreciate the historical roots of how others see them. They need to become more self-aware. Their current image stems from stereotypes which have persisted in popular culture over centuries and from the darkest side of science—the development of more effective ways of killing people.

Rosslyn Haynes of the University of New South Wales has analysed this in her splendid book *From Faust to Strangelove*, which I think should be compulsory reading for all science students. She showed that the figures of 'Doctors' Faustus, Frankenstein, Jekyll and Strangelove may be fictional but they're so powerful they've become *synonymous* with the alleged characteristics of scientists as dangerous, unreliable, authoritarian, secretive, impersonal and amoral.

Where do we go from here? Well, an awful lot remains to be done and can be done. I've used unscientific words like faith, trust and belief deliberately to expose the chasms of comprehension. As I see it, scientists need to add to the one-way street of the media by establishing and nourishing other avenues for reaching the public directly and understanding their concerns. The responsibility for mounting a credible, a skilful dialogue rests squarely with practising scientists and their professional groups.

THE PAST IS A FOREIGN COUNTRY

HELEN M. HARPER

A Highland Scot and an Arts graduate of Edinburgh University, writer HELEN HARPER came to Australia thirteen years ago. She has lived and taught in Scotland, Canada and Zambia.

The sleet fell ice-cold and foreboding over the field of Culloden on 16 April 1745. The tattered, hungry, foot-weary, ill-armed highlanders fell before the ranks of the English troops. Bonnie Prince Charlie was no match for the resolute, ruthless Duke of Cumberland. The Prince's hopes of the English throne perished on the vine that day, along with many brave Highland men. After the battle, the stragglers and the wounded were hounded to their deaths and the populace of the Highlands beaten into submission.

The death of the clan system that had formed the basis of Highland society throughout the ages was also a casualty that day. The highlanders were forbidden to carry arms and the tartan was proscribed. And so, the men were no longer of use to the chiefs as fodder for the feuds they endlessly conducted. A harsh and dictatorial rule was enforced to bring civilisation as it was then known to these rugged, savage, backward, impoverished and untamed people.

By 1792 when Australia had been settled for four years, the shameful Highland Clearances took place. The sheep was king and the redundant highlanders, now surplus to requirements, were removed to the desolate shores of the North Sea. They were told to turn themselves into fishermen. The Duchess of Sutherland saw their dreadful plight one day and was horrified, but not enough not to pass by on the other side.

Thousands of highlanders were shipped off to the colonies—mainly to Canada. No regulations governing conditions on these hulks were ever laid down, with the result that the highlanders travelled in circumstances far worse than the slaves from Africa. They were sent weeping, wailing, tearful and terrified to a land they had never heard of.

In the late eighteenth century our national poet, Robert Burns, paid a visit to the Highlands. Referred to as the Bard at Inverary, he is attributed with this comment on the Highlands:

There's nothing there but Hielan' pride,
Hielan' scab and hunger,
And if the Lord had sent me there,
'Twas surely in his anger.

Yet by the next century the Highlands became a magnet for the curious and the rather superior. Whilst gazing upon the squalor and degradation they set to and romaticised the place. The tartan was suddenly all the rage. Queen Victoria bought Balmoral Castle where she installed pipers and a tartan carpet. Prince Albert designed the new Balmoral tartan.

The Highlands became the flavour of the century—a popular playground for the rich and famous. Even Harriet Beecher Stowe of *Uncle Tom's Cabin* fame paid a visit to the Duchess of Sutherland at Dunrobin Castle. It is interesting to note that the plight of the highlanders did not strike a responsive note in her. She is reported as having been asked to write a book on their parlous condition but she refused. Maybe black slaves were more emotive. All the while the highlander was portrayed as proud, dignified, independent and possessed of a specially interesting culture.

In 1788 Captain Phillip landed on Botany Bay. He had strict instructions from the British government to 'treat kindly with the natives'. Two centuries later it is interesting and instructive to compare the similarities of the Australian and Highland experiences. When two cultures of such cosmic differences meet it would be surprising if one did not suffer an eclipse—often to the subsequent advantage of the subjugated.

The early settlers considered the Aborigines, as the highlanders so far away had been regarded by the Lowland Scots and the English, as savage, wild, backward and quite uncivilised.

There was no Culloden here—rather a series of sporadic conflicts when the representatives of the two cultures clashed. The Aborigines were driven from their lands but this was a big country. They went elsewhere.

Once settled down, the newcomers began to find the Aborigines 'interesting'. Their languages were studied—most notably in the early twentieth century by Daisy Bates, that indefatigable protector of the Aborigines. Here was a people untouched by civilisation; Stone Age people with strange mythologies and customs—some of them quite barbaric to the new Australians. They needed help and this they got in lavish quantities from the missionaries. Like the highlanders before them and at times concomitantly, the Aborigines were to be brought into the fold to reap the benefits of a better way of life.

Following on the heels of this has arrived the sentimental phase— as with the highlanders—the great rush of enthusiasm to find something wonderful and meaningful in this 'primitive' culture. So we now have the craze for Aboriginal art in all its forms. And much is made of the Dreamtime. Any day now the didgeridoo could replace the bagpipes at Union marches all over the country. Whence also has originated the latest fashion for painting our faces on high days and holidays?

A second wave of preserving Aboriginal languages has taken hold. It is an interesting exercise but not destined to further the cause of Aboriginal advancement. Long ago in the Highlands of Scotland a wise old headmaster decided that to teach in a language other than English was to close the door for many pupils to a wider world beyond.

This sentimental attitude of more advanced peoples towards those they consider less civilised is nothing new—Rousseau first coined the phrase 'the noble savage'. The surprising thing is that it can so easily be resurrected today when we know that people are people are people.

Whether it be the untamed, uncivilised barbarians of northern Scotland, the cruel, vengeful, bloodthirsty tribal life of darkest Africa or the deeply superstitious, fearful Aborigines of yore, the reaction of civilised man is the same. Repelled by the filth, the degradation, the barbarism he is, at first, filled with a messianic zeal to bring them into the present. Following on this he succumbs to romanticising and sentimentalising the situation. The closer he brings uncivilised man into his protective embrace the more frenetic he becomes in praise of 'natural' man. We must go back to this ethereal land and time where all is peace, perfect peace—a kind of heaven on earth.

Speaking as a Highland Scot it is no part of my ambition to retrace the steps of my ancestors. D'Arfeville, cosmographer to the King of France in 1583 wrote: 'Those who inhabit the North of Scotland are rude and unruly and for this reason are termed savages . . . They go with bare heads and allow their hair to grow very long and they wear neither stockings nor shoes . . . '

I have no wish to wander the hills barefoot and bareheaded even in a Highland summer. I have no wish to live in a poor hovel or in a ditch in the middle of winter. I have no desire to communicate in Gaelic when a quarter of the world's population speaks English. What would be the point? I have no illusions that life was 'better' then. How on earth could it be?

I rejoice that Culloden meant the end of feudal Scotland. I am proud that the highlanders overcame well-nigh insurmountable odds to become by the end of the nineteenth century educated, ambitious and successful whilst retaining that innate courtesy that was probably part of their downfall. Similarly, I cannot imagine that Australian Aborigines are any different. Why on earth would any Aborigine want to return to the bush to live in abject poverty, to spend hours each day searching for some roots or berries to eat? Why would their women be content to be harnessed to old men for husbands? Why would they wish to return to the old barbaric initiation ceremonies? Why would they deny their children the chance of a better life by speaking a language that only a couple of hundred people understand? It is all too limiting, especially in this wider world we now inhabit.

I don't think that the Aborigines like to be condescended to, patronised, romanticised or regarded as a curiosity in a circus or a zoo. Certainly my Highland ancestors didn't. When I see those tourists pretending to live the prehistoric life up in the Northern Territory, it makes my flesh creep. It is artificiality taken to the nth degree and demeans them as well as the Aborigines.

A few years ago in Inverness, Scotland, some idiot complained that the inhabitants were not wearing enough tartan and so maybe, perhaps, we could . . . ham it up a bit? You can imagine the reaction to that. 'Too bloody bad,' to coin an Australianism. 'The highlanders don't go around with heather between their toes any more, nor straw between the teeth. So thank you for the idea—but, no thank you.' The Aborigines and the Highland Scots have more in common than they think.

So what is the point of all this? Just that a people need dignity and it cannot be bought. It has to come through the struggle for self-improvement.

The Highland Scots seized their opportunities through education. Many families boasted by the twentieth century among their number of a teacher, a minister and a doctor. Engineers, bankers and professional occupations all paved the way for a higher standard of living—an end to the abject poverty that had dogged their forebears. A new pride built on the solid rock of achievement through their own efforts emerged.

Surely this is the way forward for our Aboriginal population. All this condescension on the part of the government and some of their own people towards the first Australians is nauseating and self-defeating. Like the Highland Scots before them, the way ahead is in education and its subsequent liberation of the body and the spirit. A people standing on the pinnacle of its own success is a source of pride to themselves and admiration to others.

Our Aborigines deserve better than a pat on the head every now and then, an army of public servants always on their heels, a host of do-gooders wailing over their plight and billions of dollars poured into a vast gaping pit. We demean them every time we imply that the only thing they can do is draw pretty pictures or cavort for the tourists or drink themselves into oblivion on faraway reserves.

Neither is land the answer. We can see that in the Northern Territory where more land has been returned to the Aborigines than anywhere else. All we hear from these remote parts is of the millions spent on alcohol. Wouldn't you take to drink if you were shunted to the back of beyond with no further purpose to your life than to live it out?

The Aborigines can look back on their past as do we Highland Scots but, please, let us shed the blinkers that can so easily inhibit any efforts to regard the huge possibilities of the future. Tennyson puts it better than most: 'For I dip't into the future, far as human eye could see,/ Saw the vision of the World, and all the wonder that would be.'

The past has gone. 'The past is a foreign country: they do things differently there.' The future beckons—to us all. Let's go! Together.

EDWARDIAN SPIN-OFFS

ROB MORRISON

ROB MORRISON, Associate Professor of Environmental Studies at Flinders University, is the Patron of the Canberra Inventors' Association and broadcasts regularly on science, technology and the environment.

Anyone with lots of books will know the problem—large books. Most modern bookshelves are spaced about 30 centimetres apart. This is excellent if you have dozens of paperbacks, but it places large books in limbo. They often accumulate in one tall shelf reserved for them all, irrespective of their subject matter. A child's pop-up book and a world atlas may sandwich reproductions of Gould's birds and the *Greening of Gondwana*. In my own shelf, a large illustrated book of Edwardian inventions stands beside the annual magazine from NASA called *Spin-offs*.

NASA's spin-offs are technological developments that have been transferred to uses different from, and often remote from, their original application in the aerospace field. They are inventions of devices, materials and techniques.

The two volumes present a curious comparison. Both have invention as their theme, but while the NASA volume deals with a flood of inventions that moved quickly to commercialisation, the Edwardian book deals with hundreds of inventions that were patented and then neglected until time and technology rendered them obsolete.

Science and technology writers often remark upon how this latter depressing fate befalls many Australian inventions. Compression refrigerators, Interscan, sequentor analysers, the photocopier, the orbital engine, and many more; we invented them all, but let them be abandoned like the Edwardian patents, or acquired by others, including the Americans, who developed them as they have developed their own NASA spin-offs into commercially viable products, which we now buy back from them.

These two alternative fates are well contrasted in the two volumes. It's worth looking into them a little more deeply to see why inventions receive such different treatments in different cultures. It's worth doing so in any case, because they contain great browsing material. Not all of the Edwardian inventions held great promise, but they were certainly appealing.

Who could not be impressed by Wacker's Improved Hat Brush, Classen's Improved Swimming Socks (with opening and closing flaps), or Koppenhagen's Device for assisting the swallowing of pills?

Deaf Edwardians could have chosen Payn's Improved Magnetic Device to restore hearing or Klaw's Appliance of Ear Shells to aid it, and they could have preserved it by using Axtell's Apparatus for disinfecting the transmitters and receivers of telephones by generating ozonised air.

Those seeking entertainment would have found it in Kelly's Improved Apparatus for Jumping, involving a trampoline concealed in the case of a grand piano; and Gillet's Appliance for enabling a performer to appear to stand upon one finger.

If the book contained only absurdities like these you could understand why they were taken no further, but there are many others like the bicycle, the neon tube, the hair dryer, vacuum cleaner and a host of other domestic appliances that were subsequently reinvented and capitalised on by others.

NASA's engineers would have loved Blunt's Improved 1901 Flying Machine, driven by steam to imitate the flight of birds, and carry an aeronaut upwards; not to mention Nicholl's Improved Flying Machine, powered by vibrations caused by the action of wind, and equipped with springloaded legs to cushion landing shock, and on the face of it some of the inventions in the *Spin-offs* magazine are just as unlikely as those in the Edwardian volume. Ironically, a number of them, such as fire retardants, forms of transport and health aids, are solutions to precisely the same problems that the Edwardians faced.

But the NASA spin-offs, while more prosaic than these Edwardian inspirations, have at least been realised. Among them the disabled of our time can find reading machines and computers which word-process in synthesised speech for the blind as well as voice-activated robots and wheelchairs for the physically immobile.

The aviation industry is well catered for with flame-resistant fabrics, improved insulation, shock-absorbent foam and navigation aids, while domestic benefits include personal computers, emergency stairwell lighting, sunglasses, pool purifiers, teflon, and ceramics.

Medical science has acquired implantable defibrillators, nuclear magnetic imaging, insulin delivery systems, thermometers that can be swallowed, and the list continues for sporting equipment, paints, house construction, automotive design and more.

There are three main differences between the two groups of inventions. One is that the spin-offs, unlike the Edwardian inventions, have not languished as bizarre ideas to be laughed at one hundred years from now. They were quickly developed and marketed and we already use many of them on a daily basis. The second difference lies in their origins. The Edwardian inventions were conceived in isolation as solutions to idiosyncratic problems. They reflect the view that, whatever foibles an Edwardian gentleman might have, he could confidently expect them to be shared by hosts of others, all eager for his solution to a problem that he perceived as all-important. By contrast, the spin-offs arose because shared work on a large project had revealed the lack of some specifically defined part or material, and the need to invent that missing part was communally recognised and supported at the outset.

And third, the Edwardian inventions tend to be complete solutions to a problem—an entire machine, even in some cases an entirely new way of building a house, down to plumbing and electricity. The spin-offs tend to be one little part of the complete picture—a better material, a new part or an improved design—each easily incorporated into a grand scheme without requiring huge modifications to it; brilliantly but narrowly conceived to serve specialised functions in a much bigger whole.

These spin-offs represent a triumph of invention, development and marketing. How did they come to be? When the astonished Americans heard President Kennedy declare that America would land a man on the moon within ten years there was much headshaking from scientists and technologists who declared that the technology of the day was not adequate to the task and that the deadline was impossible.

And yet, with national pride at stake, the moon landing became overnight a huge futuristic technological project of enormous significance. It *had* to succeed. Technology that did not exist *had* to be invented. Materials had to be developed to withstand the extreme cold of space and the heat of re-entry. Pressurised but flexible spacesuits were required. Both gravity and the lack of it had to be conquered; metals given memory, radiation repelled, physiology monitored, wastes recycled, computers refined and software developed for them. Thousands of other things which would never have been invented in isolation became absolute necessities if a man was to be landed on the moon within ten years, and many of them became spin-offs.

The Americans complain of the cost of NASA and the space program, but they neglect to include in the equation the huge boost to their economy that has come from the value of these spin-offs in a commercial market. Astronauts needed power tools to work in space. As a result, we all have access to cordless power tools and rechargeable batteries—both spin-offs. Archaeologists now explore ancient crypts using the drill designed to take uncontaminated samples from the moon. Ceramic tiles designed as heat shields for re-entry craft now provide heatproof crucibles and oven dishes. The development of home and personal computers from miniaturised computers needed by NASA has in itself been a spin-off of enormous worldwide economic and social significance.

Spin-offs have provided carbon fibre, memory metals, heatproofing, teflon, alloys and many other materials now widespread in industry and sport. They form the fabric of America's Cup yachts and Olympic cycles, the seats of which are also made from the mesh that insulates astronauts' feet in their spacesuits.

In Australia we have great ideas, invent terrific solutions and then watch them wither as their potential remains unrecognised and development money proves elusive. The Americans chased a single, overwhelming objective so advanced that it forced the development of new technologies which were then immediately adopted by others who saw their potential in the quite different fields of medicine, aviation, sport and entertainment.

A rough rule of thumb says that for every dollar spent on invention, ten dollars must be spent on development and one hundred dollars on promotion and marketing. We seem to be capable inventors, but development and marketing are our weak points; the commercial challenge remains unmet. The spin-off approach ensures both invention and development, and provides alert technologists with huge numbers of solutions just waiting to be matched with commercial opportunities.

Could we not in Australia adopt something of that approach? Do we have projects that, if not on the scale of NASA, are comparable in that they can produce spin-offs of technological and commercial benefit to us?

Take the billion trees project. At the announcement of this national project to plant a billion trees by the year 2000 pessimists dismissed its feasibility by calculating how long it took to grow and plant one billion seedlings, but almost immediately news items began to appear on direct-seeding machines. These had existed for a while, but the billion trees project ensured their newsworthiness and development. Today there are many such machines; one developed in Murray Bridge uses microelectronics designed in Adelaide. With it a person can sow 12 000 trees a day rather than plant 500 seedlings. It will seed some of the billion trees, but it is also a spin-off of that project, already hailed as an unique piece of technology with applications in other arid countries like Africa, where revegetation needs are urgent.

More recently, one only has to look at the solar challenge to see how spin-offs have developed in solar technology. Professor Green's photovoltaic cells are acknowledged as the best in the world, while electronic modules developed for one of the competitors now form part of equipment exported to Indonesia to supply solar-generated electricity to remote homes. An initial production run of a million modules is planned. Both are valuable spin-offs.

But even in this instance, we are letting the spin-offs go to others. The inaugural solar challenge race in 1987 was won by the Americans. They list their spin-off benefits in the NASA magazine. They include microelectronics, a revolutionary electric motor, photovoltaic cells, optics, lightweight materials and communications. Valuable American spin-offs from our project. They could have been ours. And the most recent challenge? The Japanese won in a car that Honda spent $10 million in developing. It contains many spin-offs in the form of innovations, but these 1993 spin-offs from our project will be Japanese. They, too, could have been ours.

Perhaps we should try this approach more in Australia. Why not the deliberate creation of a long-term national project that will produce spin-offs of commercial value and for which we retain the patents and development? What could such a project be? Let's rule out anything as grandiose as the moon landing, and do even better by choosing an aim that is at the outset really useful, rather than symbolic.

It should be in a field where we have an advantage, such as one requiring lots of space, solar energy or arid land. It should be one in which our geographical isolation and small population can be turned to advantage. It should be multi-disciplinary so as to draw upon the widest expertise, and it should be one that will meet with bipartisan political support.

It should be environmentally sound and consistent with sustainable development; national in the sense that it can involve all states and territories; and require new technology which can be broken down into diverse miniprojects that could be tackled by small departments or businesses in virtually any part of the country. It should be in a field in which world demand is growing and embrace technologies that can be readily marketed, especially amongst those countries where we want to consolidate our own economic role.

An obvious choice might be a major national project in solar energy. A massive project in water purification might qualify. So might efforts to reclaim, repair and revegetate thoroughly degraded, even salt-blighted, land. Aquaculture, effluent and waste management, control of agricultural pests or feral species could be considered. It would be easy to compile a range of projects once guidelines and directions had been decided upon, and we would not have to limit ourselves to one, but whatever project might be chosen, it should be structured and administered so as to give us the benefit of invention, development and marketing by means of spin-offs.

Much would flow naturally from a project of this kind. New areas for research, both scientifically valid and with commercial potential, would open up, and both applied and pure research would have a common focus. Links between universities and business would strengthen, but its chief benefit would be to create a structure in which Australian invention would acquire its necessary partners of development and marketing, without which it has so often languished.

Our tendency to let inventions surface and then slip away is sometimes blamed on our quarry mentality. If this is right, then the spin-off approach should suit us well. When the Americans developed their space program, they created what was, in effect, a huge quarry of innovations, new materials, and unprecedented appliances. Technologists in other fields could more or less help themselves to what was needed.

We could do the same, using a worthwhile major technological project as our focus and developing within it the kind of spin-offs, this time Australian, that work for other people elsewhere. They have now also begun to harvest spin-offs from our projects; it is time that we did too.

THE DRUMS OF HEAVEN—
BLACK HOLES AND
GRAVITATIONAL ASTRONOMY

DAVID BLAIR

DAVID BLAIR is an Associate Professor in the Department of Physics at the University of Western Australia where he is Director of the Australian International Gravitational Research Centre.

After twenty years of intense experimental and theoretical effort, astrophysicists have been able to design instruments capable of observing the gravitational wave vibrations produced whenever black holes and neutron stars form in the universe. Gravitational waves are ripples of space: in their faint sounds astrophysicists expect to be able to create images of the final shimmering moments of the formation of black holes, and the earliest moments of the big bang when all the forces were unified. To be able to listen to the birth of the universe itself, and to the final death of stars and matter as they disappear from the visible universe should be sufficient justification for spending $50 million of taxpayers' money.

But gravitational wave researchers can promise more! Gravitational waves are a completely new spectrum, a totally new window onto the universe. To explore it requires new technology, new ideas and new devices. Gravity wave research has already spawned new time standards, new magnetic sensors, ultrasensitive vibration sensors, devices for mineral exploration, magnetic brain activity monitors, and improved radars. The new gravitational observatories require new lasers, new vacuum techniques, new optical systems, and new vibration isolation techniques—all of which have enormous economic value.

Australia is at the forefront of gravitational wave astronomy. An Australia-wide collaboration of physicists, engineers and astronomers (from universities, CSIRO and industry), in partnership with teams in India, Argentina, Italy, France, the United States, Britain and Germany propose to build an observatory at Wallingup Plain, 60 kilometres north of Perth. The Australian International Gravitational Observatory (AIGO), will be a 3 kilometre by 3 kilometre laser interferometer gravity wave detector. Super-powerful, super-stable lasers will reflect off super-polished mirrors suspended at the ends of the 3 kilometre vacuum pipes. The laser beams will register gravity wave vibrations which are as small compared with an atom as an atom is compared with a human being. A network of four detectors spread across the globe will pinpoint the sources of the signals allowing optical astronomers to make correlated observations.

One hundred years ago Heinrich Hertz pioneered the search for electromagnetic waves, never guessing it would yield the electronic revolution of the twentieth century. We have no idea what the search for gravity waves will lead to, but there is no doubt that Australia will benefit from the challenge and the innovation it requires.

1 WHAT IS SPACE?

What is space? I don't mean what you get into when you go up in a rocket, I mean what we are in now. We are all in it! The universe is made of it, and in the universe it is filled up with various bits and pieces: atoms and stars and galaxies and light. But what is it?

You may say it is just nothing: it is the emptiness between which all objects exist. You might say it has three dimensions and combined with time, four dimensions. Remembering school geometry you might try to draw some axes, and think of space as a grid of imaginary lines. But doing that is a bit like equating the Earth with the lines of longitude and latitude that we draw on maps. The lines are useful in measuring space, in telling where something is in space, but certainly it does not tell us what space is.

If you can't answer my question, don't worry. Nobody knows. It is one of the deepest mysteries in modern physics. Still, we do know a bit more about space now than we did. We know some of its properties. We can measure its shape, we know it is flexible, but very very stiff. Space is the stiffest stuff in the universe. It is a billion billion billion times stiffer than diamond, the hardest material we know. Today we know how to listen to it too, because, like a drum or a metal gong, it can vibrate. We know too that you can wrench holes in space and there are plenty of signs in astronomy that these holes—black holes—are relatively common.

Our new knowledge of the properties of space was discovered by Einstein. In the last twenty years an enormous range of super-precise experiments, in laboratories, with spacecraft, and with star systems, have tested the innumerable ways that space-time can bend and distort. Einstein's theory has been proved, but as we will see, there is one enormous gap. First let us step back 150 years.

About 130 years ago James Clerk Maxwell developed a theory of electromagnetism. He was able to synthesise the knowledge of electricity and magnetism that had been built up by the earlier experiments of Faraday, and Galvani and Volta. He found a set of equations which predicted something new: electromagnetic waves. People wondered what these waves were. Could they be created in the laboratory? Could they be detected?

Heinrich Hertz began to search for these new waves in the 1880s.

He found the waves, and set the course for the electronic revolution of the twentieth century. Little did he think that radios, television, computers and the like would be created from his discovery.

2 HEAVEN'S DRUM

Einstein predicted that space was always bent and distorted by matter. He showed that gravity could be entirely explained by the curving of space. And just like Maxwell's theory predicted electromagnetic waves, Einstein's theory predicted gravitational waves.

Einstein's gravitational waves are vibrations of space. Space is heaven's drum, and gravity waves are the vibrations of heaven's drum. By the way, the name 'heaven's drum' was coined by Japanese gravitational physicists who call their detectors

pronounced 'Tenko' in Japanese and 'Tien Gu' in Chinese.

How do you make heaven's drum vibrate? For a normal drum you hit it with a drumstick. For heaven's drum we can't hit it with a stick: the skin of the drum is a two-dimensional analogy to four-dimensional space-time, and living in space-time ourselves, we are like microbes living in the skin of the drum.

But mass bends the skin of the drum. So change the mass distribution suddenly and you can suddenly bend the drum. The way we expect this to happen is in a supernova. A supernova is an explosion of a star, and the sudden collapse of its core sometimes makes a black hole. At other times pairs of neutron stars can spiral together and coalesce to make a black hole.

3 DETECTING GRAVITY WAVES

How do you detect these waves? In principle, very easily. In practice, one of the most difficult technological challenges ever faced by science. It is easy in principle, because when space vibrates, everything moves. A bell will be set ringing. The space between objects will change. It is hard in practice because of the stiffness of space. A wave in a stiff medium has small amplitude, even if it has plenty of energy. Imaging hitting a solid block of rock with a sledgehammer. You may put lots of energy into it, but the amplitude is pretty small.

We expect enormous amounts of energy to be flowing about the universe. Heaven's drum should be constantly vibrating as black holes form, as neutron stars collide. Perhaps of the greatest interest is the gravity waves that might be around from the big bang itself. These waves should still be expanding outwards, leaving the drum murmuring continuously like the sounds in a seashell. The pattern of these waves can let us image the very moment of creation.

The technology for gravitational astronomy has been developed in a painstaking struggle by experimental physicists during the last twenty years. Now it is defined. On Earth four enormous detectors are needed. They will use laser beams to make measurements to a billionth the size of an atom on mirrors 3 kilometres apart. The mirrors reflect the laser beams back and forth, and comparison between two paths at right angles can detect the motion of the mirrors.

The mirrors must be more than 1000 times better than the best telescope mirror: in reflectivity, in smoothness, and in shape. The lasers must be super-efficient, and super-stable and frighteningly powerful. The mirrors must be isolated against all terrestrial vibration to better than the billionth of the size of an atom; that is the size of the signals we expect.

Four such detectors on the surface of the Earth, with one essential southern hemisphere site, creates a gravitational wave telescope.

4 RECENT BREAKTHROUGHS

Recently representatives from all the gravitational wave research groups around the world converged on Australia to plan the southern hemisphere link in the world gravitational wave telescope. We heard that the LIGO project, directed by Professor Robbie Vogt at Caltech, is only months away from first construction, aiming to be listening in for gravitational waves by about 1997. A Russian colleague showed how you can actually image black holes in their gravitational shimmering in the moments after they are born.

Western Australian physicists announced three significant break-throughs in the creation of the ultra-low vibration environment needed for gravitational astronomy. The first is a new type of pendulum, shown theoretically to be capable of swinging for 300 years without any energy input. The second, a pendulum that takes 100 seconds to complete a single cycle. This device is capable of cutting out the lowest frequency seismic vibrations and will greatly simplify the design of gravitational wave observatories. The third breakthrough is a vibration measuring device, called an accelerometer, which uses single crystals of sapphire in its sensing mechanism. This device is one thousand times more sensitive than any commercially available devices, and will have enormous applications in aerospace technol-ogy, where it could be used to measure the vibration and acceleration of spacecraft far more accurately than has previously been possible. The European VIRGO project, which is building an observatory at Pisa, has invited the Australians to demonstrate the sapphire transducer, as it is called, on their vibration isolators.

5 THE TECHNOLOGY AND THE REWARDS

The technological requirements of gravitational wave detectors are just staggering. Already in small-scale detectors gravity wave physicists can routinely measure vibrations equivalent to about one-tenth of a milli-metre in the distance from here to the nearest star. Another way of expressing this accuracy is as the size of an atom in the distance to the moon. The new detectors will be able to measure movement of space equivalent to about one atom in the distance to the nearest star. The enormous leaps in technology require money, but will have benefits far beyond the fundamental science which is the driving force for their development.

CSIRO National Measurement Laboratories have developed mirrors of the quality we need: deviations are less than the size of an atom. Australian National University, in collaboration with the University of Hanover, has developed the first of the new generation of lasers that are required. The new detectors require the largest vacuum systems ever created, and to keep costs down they must be 100 times more efficient than conventional vacuum equipment. India has offered to provide the vacuum system for the observatory planned for Western Australia and also to provide the data processing facilities. Argentina, Britain, France, Germany, Italy and the United States will all assist and participate in the $70 million project. Many Australian companies are keen to join the project because all the technology has economic significance in totally different fields. British Aerospace Australia, BHP Engineering, VIPAC and Dynavac are all backing the project.

There are many reasons why the project will be good for Australia. Is the country willing to be bold and step into the forefront where the challenges match the rewards? We do it in sport; we do it at the races; why don't we take similar bold decisions in science?

We do not know where gravitational wave astronomy will take us. We know that it is the only way we have of explaining the big bang and of imaging black holes as they shimmer in the gravitational waves of their birth. It seems to me unlikely that gravity wave technology will lead to a new revolution like the electromagnetic revolution, but then Hertz never predicted television. Like all exploration of frontiers, we can be certain that there will be surprises.

ON BUTTERFLIES AND BABIES

J. H. LEAVESLEY

JAMES H. LEAVESLEY is a retired GP with a special interest in medical history. Five books have resulted from his many broadcasts on this subject and he now writes a regular column on medical history in the *Australian Doctor*.

I noticed recently that the physician who took me on my very first ward round ever, back there in darkest Liverpool in 1950, had received his ninth honorary degree. This was to add to his eleven medals from a retort-full of scientific societies, his Fellowship of the Royal Society, his Presidencies of the Royal College of Physicians and Royal Entomological Society, his knighthood, and, of course, his Chairpersonship of the British Mule Society.

I cannot be persuaded that any of these baubles has anything to do with that long-ago ward round at the now demolished Northern Hospital. Indeed, truth to tell, the only two things which stick in my memory of that occasion were gleaned in the urine-testing side room as we shuffled our feet and examined our cuticles while waiting for him to roll up. They were that he had appeared in the final trials for the yachting team to represent Great Britain at the 1948 Olympic Games (in the event, he misread the wind and fluffed his chances), and that he collected swallowtail butterflies as a hobby. Such was our introduction to the then Dr Cyril Clarke.

Apart from those middle-class diversions, Clarke was regarded as an undistinguished junior staff physician with hardly, one would have thought, the background or pretensions from which to garner gold medals, knighthoods and the like; but that is just where one would have been wrong. Let me explain. But stay close, because the sequence of events and the detailing of his findings is pretty tricky.

In 1952, two years after our initial joust, there appeared in an entomological journal a paper under his name on how to manually aid butterflies in their mating routine. Rather like some of England's efforts in recent Ashes series, it would seem that the labour did not have a lot going for it. Wrong again; for as it turned out, with the appearance of this seemingly artless piece of divertissement, Dr Cyril Clarke, our erstwhile tutor, had planted his foot firmly on the first rung of the ladder of fame.

The following year, using this recondite hand-pairing skill, he succeeded in crossing the yellow swallowtail *Papilio machaon* from the Norfolk Broads, England, with a related species whose ground colour is black—*Papilio asterias*—and which is common in North America. The resulting hybrid was black, and very similar to the American parent. It was also sterile, a common but not universal characteristic of hybrids, as he was later to write with some passion. In this case a back cross did prove to be possible, and in the one to *P. machaon* there was clear-cut segregation, to use the jargon of the cogniscenti. This apparently indicated a single gene difference as regards ground colour between the two species, black being dominant to yellow.

Well, fancy that, you may have thought, and you and I may well have left it there; hand pairing wild creatures is not everyone's idea of a night out. But, in company with P.M. Sheppard and later, R. Finn, Clarke doggedly persisted, for there was something in the spin-off from this bending of the natural order of things and resulting hybridisation which had begun to strike chords in Clarke's mind. He mused to himself whether or not there could be some human application to this backroom work, not, let me hasten to add, in hand coupling, but in the results it could achieve.

The experimenters decided to try their arcane skill on the phenomena of mimicry among butterflies, where one creature develops the characteristics of another for some special reason, usually as a defence mechanism. In the variety of insect they had in mind, mimicry in the field leads certain gustatory desirable butterflies to physically resemble others, the models, which are quite distasteful to predators. Models and mimics usually fly together, and birds which have sampled the disagreeable models tend also to leave the mimics alone, even though they, of course, remain highly palatable.

It is a cosy, not to say fiendishly clever, little arrangement for the colourful creatures, and the experimenters thought to try it out for themselves in their chilly and less than glamorous greenhouse cum laboratory in Liverpool. The chosen insect was a South African butterfly, *P. dardanus*, which, despite an enormous range of variable characteristics, could be hybridised fairly easily. As the human state displays a similar variation in its multiple presentations, we see for the first time an indication that Clarke's deliberate selection was slowly focusing down onto similar goings on in *Homo sapiens*.

He knew from his previous work in butterflies that a single gene controlling colour and wing pattern can be introduced experimentally into a gene complex which had had no previous experience of it. Insects of different appearance were produced, and it was shown that there was no dominance of one form over another. In the words of the geneticists, to produce this there must be 'modifiers', that is to say a major gene is influenced by a more specific minor gene, but one whose effect can only be detected if a major gene is present. In the case of the butterflies under surveillance, the modifiers accumulated to perfect the mimic pattern.

Incidentally, it was also found that mimetic wing patterns were sex linked to females, the males remaining similar to their own kind. The reason for this, it was postulated, was that courtship in butterflies is visual and females will mate only with males to whose colour and pattern they are accustomed. It is interesting to speculate that by maintaining their original marking these males appear to hold sex in greater regard than death.

Still, you would say, there is not a knighthood in all this. Right; but at this point Clarke, who all this time, of course, was earning a living tapping chests and feeling spleens, recalled work done by P. Levine many years previously, and wondered aloud if the effects of all this cross-matching of butterflies could have any parallel in the human state.

In 1943 Levine had looked at the problems associated with blood groups and pregnancy. He had observed that among Rh negative mothers who had produced rhesus-affected babies, the incidence of ABO blood group incompatible mating (for example, an O mother and an A father) was lower than expected. Thus it was felt that ABO blood incompatibility as between mother and baby was nearly always protective against rhesus immunisation of the mother. This he found was accomplished by the anti-A and anti-B antigen eliminating the foetal cells before they had time to stimulate the production of rhesus antibodies. Only group O women have naturally occurring anti-A and anti-B. In other words, ABO incompatibility protects against Rh immunisation. (Are you still with me? I hope so, because the best is yet to come.)

Clarke already knew that various genetic make-ups (or phenotypes) of the Rh blood groups are controlled by a series of closely linked genes, and that there were marked genetic interactions. This was exactly the same circumstance that had been found in the mimicry setup in his butterflies. 'Could we learn from the Lepidoptera,' he postulated, 'and by adaption, eliminate Rh haemolytic disease in humans?' The answer to this rhetorical question was to lead him on to the Royal Society and beyond.

Levine had it that Rh haemolytic disease, or erythroblastosis foetalis, is caused by male-inherited, rhesus positive, antigenic foetal red cells crossing into the circulation of an Rh negative mother, to be destroyed by the woman's naturally occurring anti-A and anti-B before they can sensitise the mother against the D antigen. In this circumstance, Rh antibodies are produced, and by dint of the resulting destruction of red cells, profound, and often disastrous, foetal anaemia manifests itself as the antibodies pass from maternal to foetal circulation.

Not only do these antibodies persist, but go on being produced in any subsequent pregnancies, so the condition gets worse the more pregnancies there are. There are three Rh antigens, but of these it was known that D antigen caused antibody stimulation in 95 per cent of cases, and so was the important one.

Aware of all this, Cyril Clarke then had his burning bush moment. It struck him that it might be possible to stimulate a mimicry situation in humans similar to the one he had initiated in the *Papilio dardanus* butterfly of South Africa; but leaving aside the hand-aided fertilisation bit, of course. He postulated that protection to erythroblastosis should be stimulated by giving anti-D immunoglobulin to Rh negative mothers where mother and baby were compatible on the ABO system.

The anti-D was to be given shortly after delivery thereby destroying any incompatible Rh positive foetal cells present in the mother's blood, and before they have had time to sensitise her. (They actually coat rather than destroy.) This would then protect future pregnancies as there would be no circulating antibodies. The potentially 'at risk' 15 per cent of mothers who are Rh negative would mimic the so-called 'normal' Rh positive status of the other 85 per cent of the population. Thereupon, model and mimic would fly together, so to speak, in unthreatened unison.

Much experimentation was done on volunteers in Liverpool and elsewhere starting in 1960. Interestingly, the first volunteers to give Rh negative blood samples were forty men recruited from the Liverpool

Police Force, who were described in the *Liverpool Daily Post* as 'men of Merseyside's mothers-to-be'. There were no ethics committees in the '60s and things were a bit gung-ho, although it was explained to these stalwarts that there was a slight risk of leukaemia from the radio-actively tagged Rh positive red cells they would receive. Clarke was later to write, ' . . . but to a man they replied' (and this really dates us), 'Doctor, we trust you'.

In the end, the result of all the experimentation was just as Clarke and his co-workers had forecast, and when completed enabled them to relegate the butterflies to merely having pins stuck through their thoraces on wet Saturday afternoons. They had done their job as a catalyst to a mind capable of lateral thinking. Those insects still alive in captivity were probably relieved to get back to mating in the time-honoured way.

As far as Sir Cyril Clarke was concerned, his seminal work on hybrids and the Rh factor led, as I say, to many marks of recognition, but one was special and unusual. For he eventually rose to the dizzy height of chairperson of that so English organisation the British Mule Society, guardian of one of nature's biggest and least understood hybrids.

He went on to write erudite papers speculating on the fertility of mules, exploding the myth that this offspring of a donkey and a mare is sterile. True enough, Clarke wrote, there are no reports of male mules being fertile, although many are obviously and rampantly potent, but a review of the literature since 1527, no less, records about thirty foals in she mules and three in hinnies, the product of a stallion out of a she ass.

The still sprightly octogenarian Clarke, whom I was honoured and delighted to meet again in Liverpool recently, feels that if his days of experimenting with butterflies are limited, the task of chromosome studies in mules is in its infancy, and bemoans the fact that, whereas humans queue up to be genetically tested, mule and donkey lovers are much too protective to lend their animals for such frivolity. 'Science is waiting for the animals,' as he put it.

But the name of Cyril Clarke will live on with his work on the Rh factor, for the resulting benefit to the sum of human happiness created by this work has been profound. The giving of anti-D in the appropriate situation is now a well-researched, refined and worldwide procedure. By dint of acute observation, logical thought and dedication we all might turn our hobbies into nice little earners, or, like Sir Cyril Clarke FRS, collect a sideboard full of well-deserved accolades.

THE 'SCIENCE' OF STUDYING

SCIENCE AND SCIENTISTS

PAUL BOURKE

PAUL BOURKE, Head of the Division of Historical Studies in ANU's Research School of Social Sciences, divides his time between research in American history and running a largescale project in the theory and techniques of research evaluation.

The nineteenth century mathematician Karl Friedrich Gauss once remarked that his friend Dirichlet's publications were few in number but that they were like jewels and were not to be counted and weighed 'as if in a grocery'. Things have changed since Gauss and Dirichlet; in our world, science has many thousands of practitioners in a hundred countries throughout the world and it has inevitably become a more prosaic activity. Nowadays, counters and evaluators of scientific publications abound. For certain carefully defined purposes, I am one of them and I should like to explain why. I shall also explain what my colleague Linda Butler and I have recently counted in our monograph *A Crisis for Australian Science?*.

Since the nineteenth century, librarians and practitioners of what is called 'information science' have been fascinated by the networks which connect scientific practitioners, by the linkages between laboratories, by the life history of scholarly publications—in general, by the way the transmission of knowledge occurs. Who read articles in the *Proceedings of the Royal Mathematical Society of London?* How did communication in scientific pursuits occur? How far did scientists replicate the experiments of colleagues? These and a dozen subsets of questions were pursued, especially in the developing schools of library science in the interwar decades of this century. Fascinating work was done in this tradition of studying what were essentially hand-counted publication and citation frequencies prompted by a librarian's interest in storing, retrieving and understanding the sources of information. Bibliometrics, as the study of publication and citations came to be called, began in the library.

The evolution from its origins in the library towards the more recent breed of evaluators occurred after the Second World War in two related but fairly distinct stages. As in most academic enterprises, pioneers stand out and an honoured name in this field is that of Derek De Solla Price, the great Harvard historian of science who began in the 1950s to make systematic use of citation counts to identify fields in which the United States, in particular, had major influence and to construct a kind of cartography of modern scientific specialisation. Another decisive contributor was Eugene Garfield, who founded the Institute of Scientific Information, or ISI as it has come to be known, in 1960 to develop routine monitoring of the major international journals in which scientists publish. ISI provided through the *Science Citation Index* and the later *Social Sciences Citation Index* and the *Arts and Humanities Index* a common body of information which could be drawn on by everybody. To this development we need to add the crucial evolution of modern computing which made it possible for ISI to turn its activities fairly quickly into machine readable data sets which others could access.

The second generation of modern bibliometrics, dominated by those concerned with various levels of evaluation rather than with intellectual cartography, built on this machine availability of data which grew rapidly through the 1970s and 1980s to the point where ISI was index-ing about 7000 of the major international journals across all fields. From a wide range of examples, let me mention just two kinds of evaluative activities which achieved prominence from the late 1970s, particularly in the last decade. First there was the routine production of science indicators in the United States by the National Science Foun-dation and by the National Institutes of Health. In these studies, pub-lication and citation counts were used to identify specialisation as they had always been and, especially in biomedical research, to provide feedback on the outcomes of funding programs and specific grants. My second example is the work associated with Ben Martin and John Irvine at the Science Policy Research Unit at the University of Sussex, the source of some of the most important policy-oriented work in this whole field. Martin and Irvine initiated two distinct levels of use of the indices of ISI: one, the study of national shares of the major indices, the second, detailed comparisons of the publications and citations of specific institutions such as, to mention a famous case, their study of radio telescopes.

The assumptions informing this evaluative use of the communica-tion networks of scientists are simple enough:

- that modern science is largely written out in journal-length communications rather than in books or other media;
- that while 'quality' in some absolute sense is not necessarily con-nected to the frequency with which scientific communications are cited, those frequencies indicate participation in the mainstream con-versations in science and the impact of specific pieces of work;
- that there is a 'pecking order' of journals in most scientific disciplines and that the study of these journals is itself an important subset of, perhaps even a substitute for, the study of publications and citations.

It is important for me to insert an aside here—to explain that what-ever the efficacy of these assumptions for fields like biomedical research, physics and chemistry, they have never been, at least in this simple form, a defensible way to approach fields like history, or literary studies or philosophy where communication through journals may represent only a small proportion of the scholarly communication and where the discourse is much less cumulative than it is in science.

Linda Butler and I began working on this material for Australia in 1988, first in connection with developing a profile of the ANU's Institute of Advanced Studies and more widely as the Australian part of a large study involving all British as well as Australian publications conducted in collaboration with Ben Martin at Sussex. This has involved over a period of years several visits by each of us to Sussex, periods here by the Sussex programmer James Skea, and a visit to Australia by Ben Martin. We have now developed a databank which includes all publications with an Australian address and citations of those publications in all indices of ISI for the period 1981 to 1992. We update this annually but, since there is about a two-year time lag for these updates, the most recent material we can add is 1992. Our procedure is to purchase the raw tapes from ISI and then to standardise the Australian addresses on the tapes—university departments can have as many as 150 variants of their addresses in this data bank. Having standardised the addresses and engaged in various other 'cleaning' activities with which users of large machine readable banks will be familiar, we undertake analysis at the level of department, institution, field of research and whole national system. All of which requires access to sophisticated computing techniques and machinery.

What should be said about bibliometrics as an evaluative tool? Providing certain caveats are kept in mind, this is useful and valuable information for the purpose of mapping national strengths and presences, for identifying the direction of the work of particular institutions and for comparing patterns of emphasis across institutions. We do not support its use in considering small units, much less the work of individual scholars—the distortions are only too obvious unless reasonably large numbers are used—and we believe that this information should always be nested in a surrounding body of other kinds of evaluative evidence, such as peer evaluation, evidences of esteem and the like. In this sense, we prefer to think of bibliometrics as a trigger to the recognition of anomaly. The work of Martin and Irvine has made clear the importance of integrating peer evaluation and bibliometric information but, where these two sources do not converge, it is important to ask why. Is it an artefact of the data or is it one of those cases where peer evaluation is itself simply out of date.

To come to *A Crisis for Australian Science?* an example of analysis at the level of total national system: the long-term origins of this study lay in the debate since the early 1980s over whether British science has shown a decline in shares of publications and citations in the SCI. The British debate was given special force by a wider intellectual issue concerning the 'decline' of the industrial and economic prominence of the country, a decline which some saw as connected to the fall away from Britain's former pre-eminence as a great manufacturing power and as a world leader in science and technology transfer. The discussion which has waged quite fiercely in *Nature* and *New Scientist*, in technical evaluation journals such as *Scientometrics* and on the floor of major conferences, had the useful spin-off of causing a progressive refinement in the methods used for analysing change over time in these quantities. My colleague and I had resolved to undertake a time series analysis of Australia's performance using the refined British methodology. We had set this in train when the second prompt occurred late in 1993 through the publication in the ISI house journal *Science Watch* of a report entitled 'Australian Science: Some Worries Mate' which published evidence of a somewhat unusual-looking pattern in which Australian publication shares did not alter across the twelve years studied but citation shares appeared to drop from the mid 1980s. We wrote a commentary on the *Science Watch* piece and advanced the schedule of the time series work we had already initiated. *A Crisis for Australian Science?* is the result.

Our detailed findings by field and subfield are by now widely reported and I will not rehearse them here. In general, we have confirmed the *Science Watch* findings. We do not yet feel entirely clear on the meaning of these figures. The simplest inference to draw would be that Australian science is declining in 'quality'. But we cannot strike an uncomplicated equation of quality with citation shares. Quality in scholarly production is a problematic notion referring to long-run impact, to intrinsic elegance and power of theory, design and demonstration. Such attributes need not show up in the short or medium term to which most bibliometric measures are confined. Citation shares can also be significantly influenced by advantageous access to the conference circuit, disproportionate membership of editorial boards, academies and the like. Beyond these matters lie structural issues of the kind which have been prominent in the British 'decline' debate such as the falling infrastructure support for 'big' science.

If we cannot speak in simple terms of quality, we *can* speak of declining impact and visibility and here we hypothesised as follows:
• that Australia's declining citation share in conjunction with a constant publications share might also be the profile of a much larger number of countries being uniformly displaced by new entrants into the international data banks;
• that some of these effects might relate to the patterns of authorship present in Australian science; for example, whether there may have been a decline in the proportion of international collaboration in the Australian reseach effort which might contribute to the overall explanation of declining impact;
• that the figures suggest changes in the role of institutions of knowledge and science in Australia; for example, universities and the CSIRO;
• that closer scrutiny of the fields and subfields in which Australian

performance seems to have changed might suggest that we have maintained our position principally in the lower cost areas of study? We also noted how frequently practitioners referred to a pressure in all sectors producing science in Australia towards work at the applied end of the discipline spectrum and towards the elaboration of science-industry links;

that there have been changes in the capacities of Australian science and Australian scientists; for example, the ageing of the group and its failure to recruit more from among women, the one major new group entering higher education and research training across this period.

We have not yet done the work to allow a systematic and well-documented analysis of all these hypotheses but we do feel fairly confident that Australia's profile of constant publications and declining citation shares is not typical of other countries with which we might expect to be compared. For the rest, the research remains to be done.

I have heard it suggested, finally, that this 'decline' doesn't matter, that Australia's comparative advantage does not lie in basic research and that we do better explicitly to shift our effort to the applied end of the scientific innovation spectrum. If the record showed that Australia had consciously and explicitly decided to alter the balance of its scientific effort towards technology transfer and applied work, this might be a persuasive view. We might argue about it but we would at least know what we were doing. There has been no meas-urable decline in our effort to 'place' science communications in the standard international places, however; what has declined has been the notice taken of that effort.

Similarly, I have encountered the objection that our monograph studies only the major international journals and does not capture science published outside that catchment, particularly in Australian journals. There are, after all, about 130 journals of science taken by the National Library which originate in Australia and only about thirty of these are in the ISI indices. There is no doubt that the journals included by ISI in the indices are heavily Anglo-American and, within that, heavily United States in origin, management and network. Is there a quality activity called 'Australian' science not captured in these indices? I am not the appropriate person to answer that but all scientific practitioners I have asked tell me to be sceptical about the claim of a science on native grounds, as it were, except in those activities such as earth sciences, agricultural sciences and some aspects of the biological sciences where Australia's naural history has given us a distinctive presence.

ANOREXIA NERVOSA

JONICA NEWBY

A veterinarian with a particular interest in the inter-actions of humans with other animals, JONICA NEWBY has been a regular contributor to the Science Show since 1994.

Anorexia nervosa is a forgotten disease. It's gone out of fashion like the decade of greed that produced it. But it's certainly still around. Although we're not seeing the steady climb in case figures witnessed in the 1970s and '80s, in the 1990s the prevalence of anorexia and bulimia nervosa, the so called 'eating disorders', is not dropping. And the frightening thing is, the girls are getting younger. Eight and nine-year-olds are now presenting with clinical disease.

Getting a handle on the real incidence of serious eating disorders is not easy, because as the disease is by its nature secretive, most figures are thought to be too low. Current Australian data suggests 0.5 per cent of young women aged fifteen to twenty have clinical anorexia nervosa—these are girls whose weight loss is so marked you can say they are literally starving themselves towards death. A further 1 per cent are clinically bulimic—they vomit regularly. Subclinical cases—still severe but not reaching some arbitrary cut-off point—account for a further 3 per cent.

So based on these estimates, which are thought to be very

conservative, we can expect at least one in twenty-five Australian girls to develop a severe, perhaps permanently damaging or even fatal, eating disorder. That's one in every classroom.

The figures are high, and you can't look at them without asking 'Why?'. Sure, most of us, particularly if we're female, are concerned with our weight, but why do some girls take it to the extremes—deny themselves food until they collapse because there isn't enough calcium in their bones to hold them up, or vomit so often the enamel of their teeth is corroded by gastric acid? The key seems to be in endemically distorted views of female body image.

Various Australian surveys have found that between 80 and 90 per cent of women are unhappy with their weight—and they feel this way by the time they are fourteen. Even six-year-olds think they are fat. South Australian researchers with the Flinders Medical Centre's Eating Disorder Unit found that 25 per cent of high school girls in the normal weight range were as intensely preoccupied with weight, shape and dieting as a group of patients who were undergoing treatment for anorexia and bulimia.

And the actual behaviours are even more disturbing. Psychology lecturer Dr Susan Paxton studied 600 Victorian teenagers. Half the girls used so-called extreme weight loss techniques occasionally—these included fasts, crash diets, vomiting, diet pills, laxatives and diuretics. Thirteen per cent used them at least once a week.

These figures point to the conclusion that anorexia and bulimia are in fact not strange at all. They are simply part of a continuum. When dieting and weight obsession are entirely normal behaviours in Western women, then those managing to make themselves ill enough to come to the attention of the medical profession are simply those falling off the end of the bell curve. As Naomi Wolfe states, 'The anorexic woman is merely doing too well, what she is expected to do very well.'

Which ones are going to fall off the curve is still an enigma and a source of concern for researchers. Anecdotally, it seems that clinical anorexics tend to have very low self-esteem, and obsessional, self-driven, perfectionist personalities. This accounts for the perception it is more common among high achievers. The problem is, most of the evidence is, really, anecdotal. For a condition which so adversely impacts on such a large proportion of the population, there has been surprisingly little good research on its epidemiology. Studies which profile the 'typical' anorexic patient have generally been conducted *after* the patient is already a clinical case. Obviously these are going to be distorted by the well-known physiological changes which accompany starvation, which can lead to depression and personality change.

To really understand what's happening, you need a view of the population before clinical onset. To date, only one longitudinal study of eating disorders has been published, and this English study looked only at the sample group twice over twelve months. And this is where the current epidemiological work of Dr George Paton, Senior Lecturer in Adolescent Psychiatry and consultant to the Victorian Centre for Adolescent Health, is so important. His team is nearing the completion of a two-and-a-half-year study of Victorian teenagers, tracking 1000 girls from Year 10 through to the end of Year 12, taking five cross-sectional views in the process.

So far, going on a diet seems to be one of the most important risk factors—although that's difficult to interpret when at any time one-third of teenage girls are on a diet, and two-thirds will have dieted at some point during their teens. But regardless of these difficulties, this is one of the first opportunities to get sound longitudinal data on eating disorders. But it still won't tell us why this weight obsession continuum exists in the first place.

Feminist writers, psychiatrists, various experts have been arguing for some time that the prime culprit is our modern image of femininity. And some of the figures do seem to bear this theory out. The average weight of fashion models, the modern fairy princesses every little girl wants to be, has plummeted over the last three decades. Thirty years ago, Miss Sweden was 172 centimetres tall and weighed 68 kilograms. Today, she's taller, but she weighs 49 kilograms. Television tells us the same story. Yes Virginia, you can be a highly successful lawyer, doctor, fighter pilot, but you must also be beautiful and thin. In a chilling scene towards the end of Robert Altman's film *Pret a Porter*, the glamorous models drop their clothes and parade down the catwalk naked. They look like nothing if not refugees from a concentration camp.

Few people will be surprised at the finger being pointed at the glamour industry. But a number of Australian researchers are increasingly concerned about perhaps a more unexpected culprit. Australians pride themselves on their public health and safety campaigns. Our anti-smoking measures are wide ranging, our AIDS prevention programs acknowledged among the world's best, and our 'fight heart disease with healthy eating and exercise' campaigns well known. And there lies the problem.

The message that healthy living means cut down on fats, lose a bit of weight, and exercise more, may be getting to the wrong group. There are fears that the campaign is inadvertently reinforcing distorted views of health and fitness among teenagers. This destructive side-effect may in fact be as important a negative in some groups as it is positive in others.

Dr Richard Newton, psychiatrist with the Royal Melbourne Hospital, has another concern. He believes that the normal range for Body Mass Index, which is used by health professionals and insurance companies, has been set quite arbitrarily too low. By this index, one-third of the population is overweight. Given the implication of dieting with eating disorders, and one can see the risk taken in telling a percentage of the normal population that they are too fat.

Dr Newton has another important point to make on the problem's impact. We must remember that although anorexia is primarily a disease of adolescents and young adults, it strikes at a time of critical psychological and physical development. The cost in terms of long-term treatment of chronic symptoms—which occur in the majority of cases—or in terms of individual suffering of young people to the point of real disability, has never even been estimated.

And that leads us to the question of health priorities. Given the conservative figure of 4 per cent of girls aged between fifteen and twenty-five suffering serious eating disorders, we can estimate that in any year there will be 16 000 clinical and subclinical cases of anorexia and bulimia in Victoria alone. And some of those will die. Although for many reasons you can't draw comparisons, it is worrying that a Scandinavian study which followed a number of anorexia nervosa sufferers over thirty years found that 15 per cent eventually died, either by suicide, or chronic complications.

Compare all these figures with the total number of HIV positive cases recorded in Victoria from 1980 to 1993—3000. Total funds spent on Victorian AIDS education and prevention work per year—$5 million. Total funds spend annually on prevention of Victorian eating disorders—$50 000.

In America, this dichotomy is marked. More people die of eating disorders in a year than die of AIDS. This is not to say there is anything wrong with focusing tremendous resources on AIDS prevention. But why aren't eating disorders getting anywhere near the same attention?

And to draw a similar point. Last year the National Heart Foundation spent $2 million on preventative programs in Victoria alone—programs which of course continually emphasise the dangers of being overweight. Where are the well-funded programs telling our young people about the real dangers of being *underweight*?

This report has been heavy on figures but has done little to give much insight into the human side. The real cost of anorexia, for those who are unlucky enough to fall off that bell curve. So I'd like to finish off with an extract from a writing by a recovered anorexic about the time when she was sixteen.

'Fortunately, my last appeal cannot be placed to most of you directly. It cannot be directed at your logic, or to wisdom gained from your own experiences.

My last appeal can only be made to your compassion.

Because for most of you, you can have absolutely no idea what it's like.

To move toward the extreme end.

When you really start to lose the battle.

Because you can't imagine what it's like when your flesh stops being part of you and becomes an obscene, slippery, loathsome, repulsive invader. When the globules of fat under your skin begin oozing and writhing and trying to suck you backwards into a black place somewhere beneath the earth. When the greasy, slimy globs of perversion surrounding a chop gain the ability to fix on you from across a room and make you need to run outside and vomit. When the consumption of a quarter of a piece of apple slice becomes a tragedy worth half an hour of hysterical tears. When your flesh turns into something that, when accidentally viewed, makes you turn away with nausea, or pinch and pummel at it as if you could just rip it all off.

Or when the bathroom scales become your saviour, your Mecca, your judge and jury to be visited hourly so you can be reassured that you are winning *just enough* to get on with the next hour of your life.

When you've finally lost. And the awful thing is that it's at this point that what you're really thinking is that finally you've nearly won. That tiny part of you that lives somewhere off to the side of the calorie counter and the *total* self-hatred, actually feels smug. It looks around and sees flesh on other women and knows that they are weak. They will never reach that wonderful slimness that you're sure you will achieve. One day. *If you can stay strong.*'

THE PLACE OF SCIENCE AND TECHNOLOGY IN AUSTRALIA'S FUTURE

DUNCAN WATTS

DUNCAN WATTS, a doctoral student at Cornell University, is working on a project he likes to call, 'The mathematical structure of social systems' (or 'Why you really *are* only six handshakes away from the President of the United States').

If you are the sort of person who listens to radio science shows or reads books about them, then you probably have an active interest in science and its relevance to the modern world. As such I'm sure you are aware of just how important a role science plays in our lives, both in shaping our beliefs and attitudes and in providing an ever-increasing flood of tools, toys and temptations with which we can occupy, improve or, conversely, destroy our day-to-day existence. One can argue all day about the benefits and evils of science, technology, research and development but one can scarcely deny the immense impact that they have had upon individuals and societies alike.

It is of considerable concern then, that the image of science in modern Australia leaves a lot to be desired. When you see articles on the front page of a national newspaper which proclaim that science is perceived by children as only for 'nerds' and by parents as an undesirable career for their kids; when the Minister for Science himself warns that Australian scientists need to lose their 'mad-professor' image; when salaries for postdoctoral students and young researchers are vastly inferior to their professional equivalents; when governments and industry argue about who should spend more money on research and development and national research budgets take substantial cuts every year, one could be forgiven for thinking that Australia is becoming a second-rate power in the race for scientific knowledge and the technology that it brings.

This is somewhat inexcusable because Australia is in fact ideally positioned to exploit high-tech industrial development, with an abundance of natural resources, a skilled local work force and a strong history of scientific achievement. We already produce good science, even if we are nerds. What we don't do very well is convert that good science to good money. All too often, an idea with significant commercial potential is snapped up by overseas investors because researchers are unable to attract local dollars. Despite a multitude of such cases where Australia has inevitably bought back its own ideas at vastly inflated prices, this trend remains a prevalent one, and it will stay this way until Australians at all levels start to take our scientific potential seriously. This means that not only must politicians and bureaucrats appreciate the immense economic power of commercialised science, but also the people who vote for them. Just as importantly, the same people must understand that no one is ever going to be in a position to commercialise their ideas if they don't have the ideas in the first place. In other words, they must be given enough support to devote themselves to front-line, fundamental research for what might be years or even decades before they get a glimpse of a cash return.

Let's start with the fundamentals. It is no great secret that the budgets of Australia's research organisations have been cut continually over the past decade. What's worse is that this attitude does not appear to be changing. Early in 1993, a CSIRO spokesman was quoted as saying that the science policies of both political parties implied further budget cuts, resulting in the retrenchment of possibly hundreds of scientists. But the problem is not just confined to dedicated research organisations, it extends to our universities as well. It is ironic that the federal government's vision of a 'clever country' should result in academics having both less time and less money to perform research. And yet, with student enrolments increasing steadily and more institutions competing for research dollars than ever before, this is exactly what has happened. The controversy surrounding the recent proposal to form a group of seven elite research universities, is a pretty obvious indication of how desperate the battle for fundamental research dollars has become.

In stark contrast to Australia, the United States, Germany and Japan all place huge emphasis on funding for fundamental science. The Germans have over two hundred government-funded institutes dedicated to excellence in research. America has over 450 universities and at $4 billion the University of Texas alone has a research budget twice that of Australia. In Japan, all large manufacturing corporations dedicate a significant proportion of their budget to long-term research, not just developing products to put on the shelf next year. I'm not suggesting that we can spend the kind of money that these economic giants can, but we sure could steal a few of their hard-learned lessons.

Speaking of lessons, if ever there was an obvious one to learn both from our own experience and that of other countries, it is that exporting raw materials and primary produce and buying them back as highly processed, value added goods is no way to make money. Instead of fundamentally changing our export base to a high-tech manufacturing level, however, the typical response of our national leaders has been to think of other objects of blame, such as world recessions, unforgiving markets, uncompromising trade competitors, lack of national identity and, not least, each other.

A more constructive approach is what is known as 'New Growth Theory', whereby a country can effectively pull itself up by its own bootstraps through encouraging developments in one area to spill over into related or even apparently unrelated areas. A good example is that of teflon and kevlar, whose inventors in the space industry could hardly have expected their useful and lucrative applications in areas as diverse as cookware and sporting goods. Naturally a high level of government stimulus would be required, and not just through investments in R&D itself. For any such program to be ongoing, the country needs a more highly educated and skilled work force, and this can only be achieved by pouring more resources into our education system, particularly tertiary education and vocational training. The vocational training is important because, in a world of high-tech manufacturing, we can't afford to be producing too many theoreticians without the practical know-how required actually to build things.

In fact this link between knowledge and merchandise has always been the Achilles heel of Australian science. And until we come to terms with it then no program of stimulating R&D will ever bear sufficient financial fruit. Therefore, the government must take the lead not only in supporting fundamental research, but also in developing products with significant commercial potential right from their early and shaky beginnings. It is simply not good enough for national leaders to scrimp and save on science and then expect industry to rush in where governments fear to tread. A recent example of this is the prototype scramjet developed at the University of Queensland. Here is a technological world first with the potential to tap into a $1 billion global market in space launch vehicles alone and yet its continued development would require all of Australia's paltry $20 million space budget. Surely, breakthroughs like this, achieved on shoestring budgets, should be enough to convince the government to spend up big, and if not, the least they could do is restructure the tax system to ensure that an investment in science is as profitable, if not more so, than an investment in say, real estate. Greater tax incentives for private investors and tax-free windows for new high-tech companies are two obvious areas for reform.

So here is the vision: Australia is a country where being a top scientist not only earns you public respect, but a whacking great salary as well. High quality fundamental research is undertaken within universities, specialised government institutes and private industrial laboratories. Australia has taken the world lead in medical and agricultural research, spaces sciences, telecommunications and environmental protection. Australia's taxation benefits have encouraged major international corporations like IBM, Marconi and DuPont to locate sizeable research and development facilities in Melbourne and Sydney. The spin-offs for Australian industry and the work force are huge. Exports are up, imports are down; Australians are educated, employed and enjoy the highest standard of living in the world.

It doesn't sound like a bad place to live does it? But even though such a dream really ought to be achievable, there is little evidence that anyone in political circles is working towards it. It is a telling fact that the 1993 election campaign was waged basically on a fear of the future: fear of unemployment; fear of the GST, and the winner was decided not on the strength of any plan or vision, but through fear of changing the status quo. Despite the existence of numerous government reports and expert opinions outlining feasible national strategies, at no stage did any of our leaders inspire us with an innovative scheme to actively rebuild our crumbling economy.

And herein lies the crux of the problem. You see, there are a great many very good ideas floating around the literature at the moment, but until they actually receive some serious attention from our national leaders, they will remain very little more than good ideas. And the problem with our national leaders is that they are politicians and politicians act on political mandates and political mandates come from the people at election time. So until the people start to care about science and technology in the same way that they care about job security and petrol prices, then politicians aren't going to care about it much either. Consequently, efforts to convince successive governments to invest more than just lip-service in a high-tech future, have been largely misdirected. Instead, you and I and everyone else who really believes that science is the long-term answer to our economic problems, should be directing our efforts not at governments who already know, but towards the millions out there who still think that science is for people who can't play football. In short, a few small, highly specialised interest groups won't change a government's approach to an election, but you can bet your bottom dollar that if half-a-dozen news polls say the same thing then both government and opposition will have a cast-iron policy out before you can say 'sleepers, wake'.

'That's all very well and good,' a cynic may proclaim, 'but exactly how do you propose that a very small group of people are going to persuade the millions of other voters to believe in something which they have consistently ignored for the last twenty or so years?' The answer is, 'How does any small group communicate with the masses when it desperately wants to get its message across?' It advertises! How did Coca-Cola become the single most recognised symbol in the entire world? How did Ross Perot manage to pull 20 per cent of the vote in the 1992 American presidential election? And how have the wars against smoking and drink driving been fought so effectively over the last few years? Through the same means as cigarette and alcohol companies made their fortunes in the first place: the power of advertising. It sounds crass, but it works. It has worked literally millions of times before and it can work just as well for science and technology. The name and aim of science must be emblazoned across Australia throughout every single available medium: prime-time television, radio, news bulletins and talkback shows, newspapers, cinemas, shopfronts and billboards. When it starts to appear as graffiti on the local shopping mall then you know the message is getting through!

And for anyone who is still sceptical about the success of such a scheme, I would ask you to remember how the environment skyrocketed to political prominence in the early 1980s. A dozen years ago, environmentalists voiced their opinions by chaining themselves to bulldozers. Nowadays, the environmentalist voice is heard in boardrooms and government committees as much as it is in the rainforests. Indeed, it is a brave politician who isn't even a little bit 'green'. How did this political metamorphosis come about? Quite simply, the people started to care. The environmentalist lobby, through a program of massive public exposure, drove home their message to a huge number of ordinary Australians, causing them to realise that the issue at stake was *their* world and *their* future in it. Ten years later Australia is one of the most environmentally conscious countries on Earth. Once the population started to speak with its voting voice, previously insurmountable barriers to change came tumbling down. The trick, then, is to make as many people feel as strongly about investing in our economic future as they do about our environment.

'Okay,' our resident cynic replies, 'so you advertise. But advertising costs money and who in their right mind is going to sponsor a nationwide campaign to promote something with a lower public image than tax evasion?' Well, interestingly enough, there are a number of large organisations who have already indicated their support for any national drive towards a research and high-tech manufacturing based economy. Organisations such as the CSIRO, the Australian Manufacturing Council, the Mining Industry Council, the National Farmers Federation and even the Anglican Church have all discovered a common interest in building a long-term strategy for Australia's future based on science and technology. Naturally, any such strategy would benefit all Australians, but the organisations that I have just mentioned will stand to reap more than most. For these organisations, money spent on advertising science is as much an investment in their own future as it is for Australia.

A recent forum in Canberra, hosted by the Institution of Engineers, proposed the formation of a national body representing industry, business, churches and education to advise on strategies for rebuilding Australia. This is undoubtedly a step in the right direction but it seems to me that in a country which invests $2 billion a year in research and development and $6 billion annually in horse and dog racing, advice is no longer enough. It is high time that both governments and the people began to realise where their priorities should lie. Such an organisation would be the perfect launch pad for a national campaign of public information about science and the role that it must play in Australian society if we are ever to see the economic recovery that we all want.

And even if you aren't a large and powerful organisation, you can still do your bit. Write to the leaders in your field, encouraging them to act on your behalf; pressure your local member of parliament or even write to the ministers controlling science, education and industry. Most of all, talk to people—friends, family and work mates—and convince them that the next time they cast a vote, it will not be cast out of fear or retribution, but for the future: theirs, ours and everyone's.